BASIC digital signal proce

Butterworths BASIC Series includes the following titles:

BASIC aerodynamics
BASIC artificial intelligence
BASIC business analysis and operations research
BASIC business systems simulation
BASIC differential equations
BASIC economics
BASIC electrotechnology
BASIC fluid mechanics
BASIC forecasting techniques
BASIC hydraulics
BASIC hydrodynamics
BASIC hydrology
BASIC interactive graphics
BASIC investment appraisal
BASIC material studies
BASIC matrix methods
BASIC mechanical vibrations
BASIC molecular spectroscopy
BASIC numerical mathematics
BASIC operational amplifiers
BASIC reliability engineering analysis
BASIC soil mechanics
BASIC statistics
BASIC stress analysis
BASIC surveying
BASIC theory of structures
BASIC thermodynamics and heat transfer

BASIC digital signal processing

Gordon B. Lockhart, MSc, PhD, DIC, CEng, MIEE, MIEEE
Senior Lecturer
Department of Electrical and Electronic Engineering
University of Leeds

Barry M. G. Cheetham, BSc, PhD, CEng, MIEE
Lecturer
Department of Electrical Engineering and Electronics
Liverpool University

Butterworths
London   Boston   Singapore   Sydney   Toronto   Wellington

 PART OF REED INTERNATIONAL P.L.C.

First published 1989

© **Butterworth & Co. (Publishers) Ltd, 1989**

British Library Cataloguing in Publication Data
Lockhart, Gordon B.
    Basic digital signal processing.
    1. Digital signals. Processing
    I. Title   II. Cheetham, Barry   III. Series
    621.38'043
ISBN 0–408–01578–0

Library of Congress Cataloging in Publication Data
Lockhart, Gordon B.
    BASIC digital signal processing.

    (Butterworths BASIC series)
    Includes bibliographies and index.
    1. Signal processing—Digital techniques—Data processing.
2. BASIC (Computer program language)
I. Cheetham, Barry.   II. Title.   III. Series.
TK5102.5.L63   1989   621.38'043   88-29533
ISBN 0-408-01578-0

Typeset in Great Britain by EJS Chemical Composition, Bath
Printed and bound in England by Page Bros. Ltd, Norwich, Norfolk

Preface

Signal processing concerns the manipulation of electrical signals for a variety of purposes such as noise reduction or frequency analysis. Because electrical signals feature in most areas of science and technology, signal processing considerations arise in a wide range of applications. These include diverse areas in telecommunications, radar, sonar, industrial process control, sound and vibration studies, geophysics, and biomedicine. Traditionally, signal processing has been concerned with 'analogue' signals in the form of voltage or current 'waveforms' and operations such as analogue filtering date from the origins of electrical science. Digital signal processing (DSP) is a more recent advance closely connected with the advent of digital technology and the digital computer. Processing signals in a numerical form using digital hardware offers significant improvements in reliability and in ease of monitoring and control over the older analogue methods. Digital signals may be reproduced and processed with guaranteed accuracy; the problems of component stability and tolerance typical of analogue systems are also substantially removed. A particularly exciting development arising from recent advances in VLSI device technology has been the emergence of inexpensive but powerful devices or 'chips' specifically designed for digital signal processing, which can be configured and programmed in much the same way as general-purpose microprocessors. This is making DSP more economic in an ever-increasing range of applications, not only as a replacement for existing analogue techniques, but also in new advanced signal processing systems such as speech or image processors with performance requirements beyond the capabilities of analogue technology.

This book provides a concise introduction to the principles of digital signal processing and provides the means of experimenting with commonly-used techniques through simple BASIC programs. Chapter 1 gives a brief survey of the BASIC language and discusses fixed and floating point systems for number representation. Chapter 2 covers essential theory including Fourier analysis and the

v

relationship between continuous and discrete time Fourier transforms leading to an introduction to the discrete Fourier transform (DFT). Linear time invariant (LTI) systems for digital signal processing are introduced in Chapter 3 and methods for frequency response analysis and system implementation are presented with the aid of BASIC programs. Chapter 4 concerns the use of digital techniques for processing analogue signals discussing aspects of the digital/analogue interface, particularly the effects of sampling and quantising analogue signals. The design of finite impulse response (FIR) and infinite impulse response (IIR) digital filters is considered in Chapter 5 and a number of commonly used approximation and realization techniques for both types are presented. Because the IIR design techniques are based on analogue filter approximations, a discussion of Butterworth, Chebychev and elliptical analogue approximations is included with reference to an appendix on analogue system theory. A brief section on the effects of fixed point finite wordlength arithmetic concludes this chapter. Chapter 6 is devoted to Fast Fourier Transform (FFT) methods and applications and includes a detailed discussion of an FFT algorithm and its implementation.

BASIC programs have been used throughout this book to illustrate the concepts of digital signal processing; we have tried to limit program length and complexity so that any program may be entered and run using a typical home computer. Some of the programs in Chapter 5 and 6 may be used with little or no modification for computer-aided design of digital signal processing systems.

Contents

Chapter 1

Introduction to BASIC

1.1 Introduction

It is likely that most readers of a book on digital signal processing will have had some experience of computer programming though not necessarily using the language BASIC (Beginner's All-purpose Symbolic Instruction Code). Although BASIC does have serious drawbacks as a professional tool for software development, it is easy to learn and use and is almost universally available on micro-computers. It is particularly useful for running small interactive programs to evaluate formulae or to check our algorithms and this will be the approach adopted in this book.

Many applications of digital signal processing involve high-speed processing of large amounts of data and require analogue/digital converters and possibly other specialized equipment. Although the 'real-time' processing power required for such applications may be beyond the capabilities of today's home microcomputer running BASIC, the principles involved can be very readily demonstrated and studied by running small BASIC programs. Many of the programs we have provided can be viewed in this light but in some cases, notably in Chapters 5 and 6, more comprehensive programs are given which can be used for designing systems for 'serious' signal processing, perhaps for operation on a larger computer.

This chapter introduces the main features of BASIC in sufficient detail to allow the reader to use and understand the signal processing programs. Different versions of BASIC abound but we have attempted to restrict the BASIC used in the programs to a subset of instructions which are legal in most variants. The programs may be enhanced in many ways: for example, by making use of machine-dependent graphics facilities for displaying signals in a more effective way than is possible with numerical print-out.

1.2 BASIC basics

A BASIC program consists of a series of numbered statements. For example:

Program 1.1 Simple demonstration

```
10 REM DEMONSTRATION PROGRAM
20 INPUT X
30 PRINT X*X
40 GOTO 20
```

This program consists of four statements numbered in ascending order to indicate the normal order of execution. Statement 10 is a 'REMark' or 'comment' statement included for program documentation purposes only and is ignored on execution. When execution starts, control passes to statement 20 which inputs a number from the user's keyboard and stores it in a BASIC variable named X. The user types a number to define the value of X and execution proceeds to statement 30 which displays the square of the value on the user's normal output device: probably the screen of a visual display unit (VDU). Statement 40 is executed next, passing control back to statement 20 to await a new number.

1.2.1 Preparing and running a program

BASIC statements may be typed from the keyboard in any order since the BASIC system will rearrange them according to their statement numbers. It is convenient to develop a new program with statement numbers in increments of 10 so that additional statements can be inserted as necessary at a later stage. Any statement may be replaced by entering a new statement with the same statement number; typing a statement number by itself will delete any statement having that number. When a program has been entered it can be checked by typing LIST. Once entered and checked a program is usually executed by typing RUN. Program 1.1 will continue to run indefinitely as it contains no statement for halting execution. Normally the computer will have some external means of terminating such a program, such as an ESCAPE key.

1.3 BASIC variables

BASIC variables, such as X in Program 1.1, are used to store and manipulate numbers during execution of a program and play the same role as algebraic variables. Names of variables are often restricted to two characters, the first of which must be a letter, and this convention should be adopted if programs are to run on a range of different computers. For example:

Y,Z,ZZ,A1,K9

are all valid names for BASIC variables.

Strings of characters such as 'RED' or '∗ ERROR ∗' can be represented by BASIC 'string variables'. String variable names are usually distinguished by the dollar sign, $, as the last character; for example:

A$, X3$, ZZ$

are valid string variable names in BASIC.

1.4 Input

The INPUT statement allows the user to give values to variables during program execution by typing from the keyboard. More than one variable can be assigned in one input statement. For example, the following statement allows the user to type in two numbers and a character string which become the current values of V1, X and Z$ respectively:

30 INPUT V1, X, Z$

Numbers can be entered as integers such as 1, 3479, −50 or real numbers such as 24.412 or −35.92315.

1.4.1 Read

It can be useful to prepare a list of numbers in advance for reading successively into BASIC variables. The READ statement assigns values to variables from a data block included in the program itself. The following modified version of Program 1.1 uses a READ statement to compute the squares of the even integers from 10 to 20.

Program 1.2 Demonstration of READ

```
10 REM DEMONSTRATION PROGRAM
20 READ X
30 PRINT X*X
40 GOTO 20
50 DATA 10, 12, 14, 16, 18, 20
```

The first time statement 20 is executed the value 10 is assigned to X, the second time, 12 and so on causing 100, 144, ..., 400 to be printed out in sequence. In general, more than one data statement may be included in a program and they are read in the order they appear. If data becomes 'exhausted' then an error message will be displayed. This will happen in Program 1.2 when a further READ is attempted after '20' has been read in by the READ statement.

1.5 Output

The PRINT statement provides the normal means of displaying numbers and character strings on the user's output device. For example:

200 PRINT "RESULTS ARE", X, Y, X+Y, Q1/RA

When this statement is executed the character string in quotes is displayed followed by the current values of X, Y, X + Y, and Q1 divided by RA. For example, if X = 2, Y = 1.8, Q1 = 5 and RA = 2 then execution of statement 200 will display:

RESULTS ARE 2 1.8 3.8 2.5

Items in the PRINT list are normally displayed on the same line and there are various conventions for formatting within the line. A semicolon is commonly used instead of a comma for separating items and minimizes the number of spaces which appear between items in the displayed output.

1.6 BASIC arithmetic

Arithmetic expressions consisting of constants, variables and functions such as SIN, COS, LOG, etc. combined with +, −, * (multiply), / (divide) and ^ (to the power of) are interpreted as in ordinary mathematics. The use of parentheses is recommended for clarity in complicated expressions. Evaluation of an expression and assignment of its current value to a variable is achieved by assignment statements such as:

20 LET X = 3 + 4*Y
30 LET A$ = "YES"

If Y = 2 when statement 20 is executed, the value of X becomes equal to the arithmetic expression; in this case $3 + 4 \times 2 = 11$. Statement 30 stores the character string YES in A$. A 'recursive' statement such as:

10 LET X = X + 1

modifies the current value of a variable, in this case by increasing the current value of X by 1. Use of LET is usually optional and statement 10 above may be expressed simply as:

10 X = X + 1

1.7 Conditional branches

The power of any digital computer depends on its ability to change the sequence of instructions to be executed according to whether or not some test condition is satisfied. In BASIC, this decision-making ability is provided by the IF statement. For example:

300 IF X > 3 THEN PRINT "OK"

If the current value of X exceeds 3 then the PRINT is executed; otherwise control simply passes to the next statement. BASIC provides the 'conditional operators' listed in Table 1.1.

Table 1.1 Conditional operators available in BASIC

=	equals
<>	is not equal to
<	is less than
<=	is less than or equal to
>	is greater than
>=	is greater than or equal to

If a statement number is supplied after THEN this is taken as a GOTO. For example:

20 IF PQ < > X1 THEN 305
30 STOP

If PQ is not equal to X1 the next statment executed will be 305; otherwise statement 30 is executed and the program stops.

1.7.1 Loops

In BASIC, program 'loops' of instructions for repetitive execution can be constructed using IF and GOTO statements but are more conveniently arranged using the FOR/NEXT construction. A loop starts with a FOR statement and has the general form:

FOR X = S TO E STEP I

It is terminated by the statement:

NEXT X

where X is the same 'loop control variable' used in the FOR statement. In general, S, E or I may be arithmetic expressions and X assumes a range of values starting at S and increasing in steps of I until E. The use of a FOR/NEXT loop is illustrated by Program 1.3 which computes the average of ten numbers:

Program 1.3 Demonstration of a loop

```
10 REM AVERAGE OF 10 NUMBERS
20 S = 0
30 FOR N = 1 TO 10
40 INPUT X
50 S = S + X
60 NEXT N
70 PRINT "AVERAGE IS"; S/10
```

The first time the loop formed by statements 30 to 60 is executed, the FOR statement 30 assigns the value 1 to the loop control variable N, and S becomes the value of the number input at statement 40. The NEXT statement 60 passes control back to statement 30 since $N \le 10$ and the next loop execution begins with $N = 2$. S now becomes the sum of 2 numbers. The process continues with repeated execution of the loop until $N = 10$ when S becomes the sum of 10 numbers whereupon the NEXT statement passes control to statement 70 and the average of the 10 numbers is printed.

1.8 Functions

BASIC provides for the common mathematical functions listed in Table 1.2. These can be incorporated in arithmetic expressions, although care must be taken to ensure that the value of the argument, X, always lies in a range for which the function is well-defined. For example, if $X < 0$ then SQR(X) will generate an error message. There may also be restrictions placed on the maximum magnitudes of the argument which can be used.

The INT function can be used to 'round off' the value of a variable to the nearest integer. For example:

$$Q = INT(X + 0.5)$$

If X is 0, 0.1 or -0.7 then Q will become 0, 0 or -1 respectively. Also, the statement:

$$Q = INT(1000*X + 0.5)/1000$$

Table 1.2 Maths functions available in BASIC

Basic function	Meaning	Comment
SIN(X)	sin(X)	X in radians
COS(X)	cos(X)	X in radians
ATN(X)	arctan(X)	result in radians
SQR(X)	$\sqrt{X}$	usually faster than X^0.5
LOG(X)	$\log_e X$	natural logarithm
EXP(X)	e^X	
ABS(X)	$\lvert X \rvert$	magnitude of X
INT(X)	largest integer less than X	

rounds X to 3 decimal places.

In addition to the 'built-in' functions listed in Table 1.2, BASIC also provides for user-defined functions. For example:

100 DEF FNA(X) = 0.5*(EXP(X) + EXP(−X))

defines the function FNA(X) as cosh(X). Whenever FNA(X) appears in a BASIC expression, it will be evaluated as cosh(X) according to this definition using the current value of X. X may be replaced by any arithmetic expression. For example if Y = −3, FNA(Y+2) will evaluate cosh (−1). The position of the DEF statement in a program may be subject to restriction since it is a function definition rather than an executable statement. Other function definitions can be made using FNB, FNC, FND, ... etc. as names.

1.9 Arrays

An array is a set of indexed variables. For example, the set of numbers:

$$\{x_1, x_2, \dots x_5\}$$

may be stored in the five 'elements' of an array X:

X(0), X(1), ..., X(4)

Index values in BASIC are non-negative integers and array elements may be referenced by an index which itself is a BASIC variable or expression. If the index N = 0, then X(N) specifies the first element of the array X but if N is changed so that N = 4 then a subsequent reference to X(N) will specify X(4). This facility to reference array elements in a general way becomes highly efficient when manipulating large sets of data and is the main advantage of the array concept. An array must normally be 'dimensioned' using a

DIM statement at the beginning of a program before its elements can be referenced. Such a 'declaration' directs the BASIC system to allocate memory to the array. For example, the statement:

500 DIM X(100),YI(300)

dimensions arrays X and YI permitting reference to elements 0 to 100 of X and 0 to 300 of Y. Often, dimension statements can be written in the form DIM X(NS) where NS is a BASIC variable or expression although there may be restrictions placed on this type of usage. Most BASIC systems allow arrays of more than one dimension to be declared. For example:

10 DIM X(10,20)

declares X as an 11 by 21 matrix of elements each of which can be referenced by a row and column index. Thus, X(0,4) is the element located on the first row in the fifth column of the matrix.

1.10   Subroutines

There is frequently a need to execute an identical sequence of statements at different parts of the same program. GOSUB and RETURN statements provide the means of branching from a main program to a subroutine and subsequently returning to the statement following the branch. Since subroutines are usually positioned at the end of a main program, the main program should always be terminated by a STOP or an END statement to prevent illegal execution of a subroutine following the main program.

1.10.1   A subroutine for defining the values of an array

Programe 1.4 illustrates various BASIC features and incorporates a subroutine for defining the values of an array. It will be convenient to use this subroutine in later programs for defining digital signals. Note the use of the colon for separating different statements having the same statement number; this is permitted in most versions of BASIC.

The main program in Program 1.4 extends only from statements 5 to 60. An array X is declared with 101 elements, the number of array elements, NS, is requested and subroutine 10000 is called to define the array values according to one of five possible options. The main program then prints out the array values from elements 0 to (NS − 1). As the array X must be dimensioned in the calling program this sets a limit to the largest value of NS which can be used; in this case 101.

On entry to subroutine 10000, the elements of X are set to zero and the user selects a definition of array values by typing two characters which are assigned to the string variable A$. A$ is then tested in statements 10040 to 10080 by a series of IF statements to determine which of the five options apply whereupon control passes to the relevant section of code. If the user selects the 'zero' option by typing ZE then statement 10080 returns control immediately back to the calling program and the values of all elements of X will be zero. The other options allow the user to define an 'impulse' sequence (IP), a 'unit pulse' (UP) starting and ending at given elements, a 'sine wave' (SN) or user-defined values (ME).

Program 1.4 SETARRAY: definition of array values

```
5 REM SETARRAY
10 DIM X(100)
20 PRINT "NUMBER OF ELEMENTS"
30 INPUT NS
40 GOSUB 10000
50 FOR N=0 TO NS-1 : PRINT X(N); : NEXT N
60 END
10000 REM - - ARRAY DEFN. SUBROUTINE - -
10010 FOR N=0 TO NS-1 : X(N)=0 : NEXT N
10020 PRINT "SEQUENCE TYPE ";
10030 INPUT A$
10040 IF A$="IP" THEN 10100
10050 IF A$="UP" THEN 10120
10060 IF A$="SN" THEN 10170
10070 IF A$="ME" THEN 10250
10080 IF A$="ZE" THEN RETURN
10090 PRINT "??" : GOTO 10020
10100 REM - - - UNIT IMPULSE - - -
10110 X(0)=1 : RETURN
10120 REM - - - UNIT PULSE - - -
10130 PRINT "STARTING/ENDING SAMPLE NOS.";
10140 INPUT SN,EN
10150 FOR N=SN TO EN : X(N)=1 : NEXT N
10160 RETURN
10170 REM - - - SINE WAVE - - -
10180 PRINT "PERIODS OVER";NS;"SAMPLES";
10190 INPUT PR
10200 PRINT "NO. SAMPLES DELAY";
10210 INPUT DL
10220 W=8*ATN(1)*PR/NS
10230 FOR N=0 TO NS-1 : X(N)=SIN(W*(N-DL)) : NEXT N
10240 RETURN
10250 REM - - - - ME - - - -
10260 PRINT "STARTING/ENDING AT SAMPLE NOS.";
10270 INPUT SN,EN
10280 FOR N=SN TO EN
10290 PRINT "VALUE NUMBER";N;
10300 INPUT X(N)
10310 NEXT N
10320 RETURN
```

1.11 Graphics

Later chapters deal extensively with sampled signals in the form of number sequences. The properties of signals represented in this way are often difficult to appreciate when printed out as lists of array values and graphical displays can be much more effective. Unfortunately, there is a lack of standardization for BASIC graphics and every microcomputer type tends to have its own graphics statements and definitions. Your particular microcomputer manual should be consulted to find out how to display array values in graphical format as this facility will greatly enhance some of the signal processing programs presented in this book.

1.12 Number representation

The accuracy and range of numbers that can be manipulated by a digital system or computer program depends on the number of binary digits (bits) allocated to each number and the method adopted for number representation. Fixed and floating point representations are the most common methods.

1.12.1 Fixed point numbers

If r bits are available then, in fixed point number representation, a fixed number of bits, say n, are allocated to the fractional part of the number and the remaining bits, $(r - n)$ to the integer part. The binary equivalent of the decimal point is therefore located in a fixed position n bits from the least significant bit. This type of representation will be referred to as 'Qn format'.

Negative numbers may be represented by adopting the 'two's complement' convention in which case the binary number having bits $\{b_{r-1}, b_{r-2}, \ldots b_0\}$ has the value:

$$2^{-n}(-b_{r-1}2^{r-1} + b_{r-2}2^{r-2} + \ldots + b_1 2 + b_0)$$

as an r-bit fixed point number in Qn format. For example, if $r = 8$ and $n = 4$, the values of 01010101 and 10101010 are 5.3125 and -5.375 respectively. If $n = 0$ only integers are represented.

Fixed point number representations permit arithmetic operations to be performed relatively quickly and easily using simple digital hardware and/or software. The two's complement convention allows negative numbers and subtraction to be accommodated with little additional complexity over that required for positive numbers and addition. Fixed point number representations are often used in real time digital signal processing systems as will be discussed in

Chapter 5. However they are not suitable for general use in BASIC programming because of severe range limitations and problems of accuracy when small magnitudes are represented.

1.12.2 Floating point numbers

Some of the disadvantages of fixed point numbers can be overcome using 'floating point' representation. In this case, the bits available for each number are divided between a fixed point number m referred to as a 'mantissa', and a positive or negative integer x referred to as an 'exponent'. The value of the floating point number is taken as mb^x where b is the 'base', normally equal to two. The mantissa if often a fixed point two's complement number in the range ± 1. For example if $m = 0.9$, $x = 7$ and $b = 2$, then m and x are stored as fixed point numbers and the value represented is $0.9 \times 2^7 = 115.2$. Floating point representations can accommodate a very wide range of numbers and offer approximately the same percentage accuracy to all numbers within this range. For this reason, the floating point system is normally used for internal representation of numbers in BASIC although some versions of BASIC offer integers as an optional extra.

Chapter 2

Continuous and discrete time signals

2.1 Introduction

A signal can be described as a measurable variation in some physical quantity. This variation normally conveys information. Physical quantities such as temperature, pressure, light intensity, voltage, current and many others can produce measurable variations. The information conveyed may be very simple, for example the existence of some fault in a piece of machinery as indicated by an increase in temperature, or it may be quite complicated as for a spoken message conveyed by airborne pressure variations, that is, sound. Signals can be transferred from one physical quantity to another, and it is often convenient to convert them into voltage or current variations referred to as electrical signals. An example of such a signal is the varying voltage obtained from a microphone with speech input. Segments of this signal may be represented by graphs of voltage against time as illustrated in Figure 2.1. The signal is said to be continuous as the microphone voltage may take any amplitude between two extremes, and may be measured at any point in time. Continuous electrical signals are often referred to as 'analogue' signals since the voltage or current is the electrical analogue of a continuously variable physical quantity.

When a signal is sampled by measuring its value at discrete points in time, the sequence of sample values produced may be referred to as a 'discrete time signal'. Sampling points are normally separated by equal intervals of time, say T seconds, as will be assumed throughout this book. Denoting by $x[n]$ the sample at time nT, the sequence is:

$$\{\ldots, x[-2], x[-1], x[0], x[1], x[2], \ldots\} \qquad (2.1)$$

which is referred to for short as $\{x[n]\}$ or 'the sequence $x[n]$'. According to this notation, $\{x[n-k]\}$ denotes the sequence whose value at $t = nT$ is $x[n-k]$ and is therefore $\{x[n]\}$ with each sample shifted k places to the right or delayed by k sampling intervals. Segments of discrete time signals may be represented in graphical form as illustrated in Figure 2.2 for the sequence $x[n]$ obtained by sampling $v(t)$ in Figure 2.1 at intervals of $T = 0.0001$ seconds. The

12

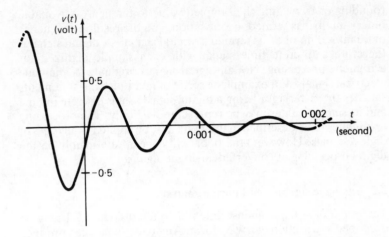

Figure 2.1 Graph of voltage against time representing a segment of an analogue signal

sampling rate, often referred to as f_s, is $1/T$ samples per second or Hertz (Hz). In this example $f_s = 10\,000$ Hz.

Analogue-to-digital conversion (ADC) devices are readily available for producing binary numbers to represent sampled voltages or currents. The accuracy of the conversion is determined by the 'wordlength' of the device, i.e. the number of bits available for each binary number, typically between 8 and 16. The process of

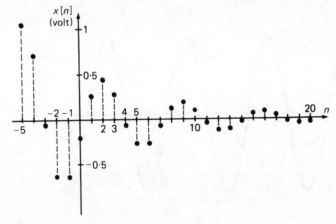

Figure 2.2 Segment of a discrete time signal $\{x[n]\}$

rounding or truncating the sampled value to the nearest available binary number is termed 'quantisation' and the resulting sequence of quantised numbers is termed a 'digital signal'. A digital signal is therefore a discrete time signal with each sample digitized for arithmetic processing. Not all digital signals originate as analogue electrical signals. For example, a series of monthly bank statements satisfies the criteria for being a digital signal as it is discrete in time and its sample values may be represented digitally. The processing techniques to be described in this book may be applied to all types of digital signals. However, the book will concentrate mainly on the digital processing of converted analogue signals.

2.2 Analogue signals and Fourier analysis

The graph of voltage against time illustrated in Figure 2.1 may be described as a section of a waveform. Analogue signals can produce an infinite variety of different waveforms which can be very complicated and difficult to describe. Fourier analysis is used to relate such waveforms to a range of simpler waveforms referred to as sinusoids. A sinusoid is a waveform whose voltage $x(t)$ at time t is given by the formula:

$$x(t) = A \cos (\Omega t + \phi) \qquad (2.2)$$

where A is the amplitude (in volts), Ω is the angular frequency in radians per second and ϕ is the phase angle in radians. Note that the symbol Ω is adopted here to allow ω to be used for relative frequency (See Section 2.3).

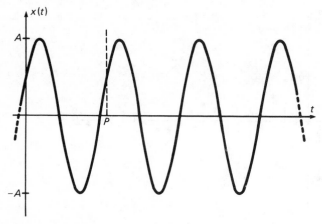

Figure 2.3 Segment of a sinusoidal waveform

Figure 2.3 shows a short segment of the sinusoidal waveform defined by Equation (2.1) which in theory extends from $t = -\infty$ to $t = +\infty$. The waveform is periodic in that a fundamental cycle from $t = 0$ to $t = P$ is repeated at intervals of P seconds, where $P = 2\pi/\Omega$. The frequency of repetition is $1/P$ cycles per second or Hertz (Hz). The phase angle ϕ determines which point on the waveform occurs at time $t = 0$.

2.2.1 Periodic signals and Fourier series

Many signals are encountered which are periodic but not sinusoidal. Examples are given in Figures 2.4 and 2.5. A periodic signal $x(t)$, with period P seconds, satisfies:

$$x(t + P) = x(t) \text{ for all values of } t \text{ from } -\infty \text{ to } +\infty \qquad (2.3)$$

Under certain conditions normally satisfied by signals of practical interest, the periodic waveform $x(t)$ may be expressed as the sum of a series of sinusoids, i.e.:

$$x(t) = A_0 + \sum_{n=1}^{\infty} A_n \cos(n\Omega_0 t + \phi_n) \quad \text{(Fourier series)} \qquad (2.4)$$

This is known as a Fourier series with a fundamental frequency of Ω_0 radians/second. When $x(t)$ has period P seconds, $\Omega_0 = 2\pi/P$. The Fourier series amplitude coefficients A_0, A_1, A_2, ... and phase coefficients ϕ_1, ϕ_2, ϕ_3, ... are constants which characterize $x(t)$. Therefore $x(t)$ has been expressed as the sum of a constant A_0 and

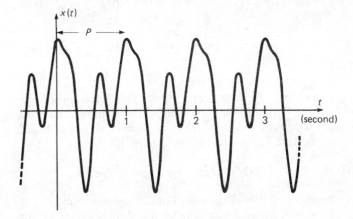

Figure 2.4 Segment of a non-sinusoidal periodic waveform

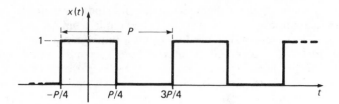

Figure 2.5 Square waveform of period P seconds

sinusoids of angular frequency Ω_0, $2\Omega_0$, $3\Omega_0$, and so on. The sinusoid at angular frequency Ω_0, i.e. $A_1 \cos{(\Omega_0 t + \phi_1)}$, is called the fundamental frequency component of $x(t)$. The other sinusoids are called harmonic components, the component at angular frequency $2\Omega_0$ being the second harmonic, the component at $3\Omega_0$ being the third harmonic and so on. It is often convenient to re-express Equation (2.4) in complex form by means of the relation:

$$\cos x = (e^{jx} + e^{-jx})/2$$

where $j = \sqrt{-1}$. The complex (or exponential) Fourier series which results is:

$$x(t) = A_0 + \sum_{n=1}^{\infty} \tfrac{1}{2} A_n [e^{j(n\Omega_0 t + \phi_n)} + e^{-j(n\Omega_0 t + \phi_n)}]$$

$$= \sum_{n=-\infty}^{\infty} C_n e^{jn\Omega_0 t} \quad \text{(complex Fourier series)} \quad (2.5)$$

where $C_0 = A_0$, $C_n = \tfrac{1}{2} A_n e^{j\phi_n}$ and $C_{-n} = \tfrac{1}{2} A_n e^{-j\phi_n}$

$$\text{for } n = 1, 2, 3 \ldots \quad (2.6)$$

The Fourier series (2.4), or equivalently (2.5), has an infinite number of terms. Waveforms for which all but a finite number of these terms are zero are said to have finite bandwidth. An example is shown in Figure 2.4 which has the Fourier series

$$x(t) = 1 + 4\cos{(2\pi t)} + \cos{(4\pi t - \pi/2)} + 2\cos{(6\pi t + \pi/3)} \ (2.7)$$

For some idealized waveforms, the Fourier series has an infinite number of non-zero terms. This is true for the idealized square wave illustrated in Figure 2.5 which can be shown (see Problem 2.3) to have the Fourier series:

$$x(t) = \frac{2}{\pi}\left(\frac{\pi}{4} + \cos(\Omega_0 t) + \frac{1}{3}\cos(3\Omega_0 t + \pi)\right.$$

$$\left. + \frac{1}{5}\cos(5\Omega_0 t) + \frac{1}{7}\cos(7\Omega_0 t + \pi) + \ldots\right) \quad (2.8)$$

Such idealized waveforms are very useful as mathematical concepts and may be approximated by real analogue signals. The closeness of the approximation will always be limited to some extent by finite bandwidth constraints imposed by practical systems. The effect of restricting the bandwidth of a periodic waveform whose Fourier series is known may be assessed using Program 2.1 which is able to tabulate the sum of any finite bandwidth Fourier series over a range of values of t.

Program 2.1 FSUM: Fourier series summation

```
10   REM FSUM .. FOURIER SERIES SUMMATION
20   DEF FNR(X) = INT(X*1000+0.5)/1000
30   DIM W(20), A(20), P(20)
40   PRINT"ENTER NUMBER OF SINUSOIDS:";
50   INPUT K
60   INPUT "ENTER A0:";
70   INPUT A0
80   PRINT "FOR EACH SINUSOID, ENTER:"
90   PRINT "FREQ(RAD/SEC), AMPL(V), PHASE(RAD)"
100  FOR N=1 TO K
110    INPUT W(N), A(N), P(N)
120  NEXT N
130  PRINT"OK"
140  PRINT"ENTER INITIAL & FINAL TIMES(SEC):-"
150  INPUT TI,TF
160  PRINT"ENTER TIME STEP (SEC):";
170  INPUT TS
180  PRINT"TABLE OF RESULTS:-"
190  PRINT"TIME(SEC)","VOLTAGE(V)"
200  T=TI
210  V=A0
220  FOR N=1 TO K
230    V=V+A(N)*COS(W(N)*T+P(N))
240  NEXT N
250  PRINT FNR(T),FNR(V)
260  T=T+TS
270  IF T<=TF THEN GOTO 210
280  STOP
```

```
Sample run

ENTER NUMBER OF SINUSOIDS:? 3
ENTER A0:? 1
```

```
FOR EACH SINUSOID, ENTER:
 FREQ(RAD/SEC), AMPL (V), PHASE(RAD)
 ?   6.283      , 4      ,  0
 ?  12.566      , 3      ,  -1.571
 ?  18.850      , 2      ,  1.047
OK
ENTER INITIAL & FINAL TIMES(SEC):-
? -0.5 , 3.5
ENTER TIME STEP (SEC):? 0.01
TABLE OF RESULTS:-
TIME (SEC) VOLTAGE(V)
   -0.50    -4.001
   -0.49    -3.375
   -0.48    -2.515
   -0.47    -1.742
      .        .
      .        .
      .        .
    3.5     -4.002
```

Program notes

(1) Function FNR(X) is defined at statement 20 for rounding to three decimal places.
(2) The sample run tabulates $x(t)$ as defined by its Fourier Series (2.7). The output is plotted in Figure 2.4.

2.2.2 *Aperiodic signals and Fourier transforms*

Aperiodic (non-periodic) signals do not have Fourier series and it is therefore necessary to relate them to sinusoids in a different way. It is convenient to restrict attention initially to signal waveforms $x(t)$ which satisfy the condition:

$$\int_{-\infty}^{\infty} |x(t)|\, dt \quad \text{is finite} \tag{2.9}$$

Such waveforms are typically those which are non-zero for a limited period of time or start at $t = 0$ and decay towards zero as time progresses. The Fourier transform $X(j\Omega)$ of a signal $x(t)$ which satisfies (2.9) is defined as:

$$X(j\Omega) = \int_{-\infty}^{\infty} x(t)\, e^{-j\Omega t}\, dt \quad \text{(Fourier transform)} \tag{2.10}$$

and is a finite complex number for any value Ω in the range $-\infty$ to ∞. It may be shown that (see References [1] or [2]):

$$x(t) = \frac{1}{2\pi} \int_{-\infty}^{\infty} X(j\Omega)\, e^{j\Omega t}\, d\Omega \quad \text{(Inverse Fourier transform)} \tag{2.11}$$

When $x(t)$ is real for all values of t:

$$X(-j\Omega) = \int_{-\infty}^{\infty} x(t)\, e^{j\Omega t}\, dt = X^*(j\Omega) \qquad (2.12)$$

which is the complex conjugate of $X(j\Omega)$. Writing $X(j\Omega)$ in polar form as:

$$X(j\Omega) = R(\Omega)\, e^{j\theta(\Omega)} \qquad (2.13)$$

it follows that $X(-j\Omega) = R(\Omega)\, e^{-j\theta(\Omega)}$ and therefore:

$$x(t) = \frac{1}{2\pi} \int_0^{\infty} R(\Omega)\, (e^{j\theta(\Omega)}\, e^{j\Omega t} + e^{-j\theta(\Omega)}\, e^{-j\Omega t})\, d\Omega$$

$$= \frac{1}{\pi} \int_0^{\infty} R(\Omega) \cos(\Omega t + \theta(\Omega))\, d\Omega \qquad (2.14)$$

This equation gives some insight into the physical meaning of $X(j\Omega)$ as a complex valued 'spectral density' function whose magnitude and phase determine how the characteristics of $x(t)$ are distributed across a continuous spectrum of sinusoidal frequency components with frequency Ω ranging from 0 to ∞. When $x(t)$ is a voltage, $R(\Omega)$ is in units of volts per unit bandwidth. $(R(\Omega))^2$ in volts-squared per unit bandwidth indicates how the energy of $x(t)$ is distributed in the frequency domain and is referred to as the 'energy

Figure 2.6 Sand distributed along a beam to illustrate the concept of density

spectral density'. The concept of spectral density is analogous to many other uses of the term density including the most common which is mass per unit volume. A simpler analogy is mass per unit length as obtained when a quantity of sand is distributed along a

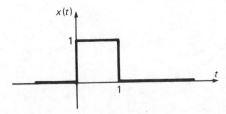

Figure 2.7 'Single pulse' waveform

beam or ruler as illustrated in Figure 2.6. Although the quantity of sand at a single point along the beam is negligible a significant measurement of mass per unit length may be obtained at that point.

Consider the single pulse waveform $x(t)$ shown in Figure 2.7. Its Fourier transform is:

$$X(j\Omega) = \int_0^1 1\,e^{-j\Omega t}\,dt$$

When $\Omega = 0$, $X(j\Omega) = 1$. Otherwise:

$$X(j\Omega) = \frac{1}{-j\Omega}\,(e^{-j\Omega} - 1) = \frac{e^{-j\Omega/2}}{-j\Omega}(e^{-j\Omega/2} - e^{j\Omega/2})$$

$$= (1/\Omega)\,e^{-j\Omega/2} \cdot 2\sin(\Omega/2) = e^{-j\Omega/2}\,\mathrm{sinc}\,(\Omega/2)$$

where:

$$\mathrm{sinc}\,(\theta) = \begin{cases} \dfrac{\sin\theta}{\theta} & : \quad \theta \neq 0 \\[2mm] 1 & : \quad \theta = 0 \end{cases} \tag{2.15}$$

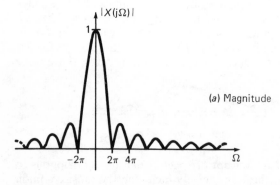

(a) Magnitude

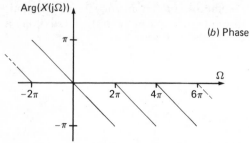

(b) Phase

Figure 2.8 Magnitude and phase spectra of single pulse waveform

Graphs of the magnitude and phase of $X(j\Omega)$ are given in Figures 2.8(a) and 2.8(b). A plot of the energy spectral density, $(\text{sinc}(\Omega/2))^2$, would indicate that the pulse's energy is distributed across an infinite frequency range but with the greatest concentration between $\pm 2\pi$ radians/second.

2.2.3 Fourier transforms of periodic waveforms

For completeness it would be useful to apply the Fourier transform to periodic as well as aperiodic signals. However, a periodic signal cannot satisfy Equation (2.9) and therefore its Fourier transform does not exist in the normal sense. This restriction can be circumvented using the mathematical concept of a 'Dirac delta function', denoted $\delta(u)$, which is a function (strictly the term 'generalized function' should be used) of real variable, u say, with the following two properties:

$$\delta(u) = 0 \text{ for } u \neq 0 \qquad (2.16)$$

$$\int_{-\infty}^{\infty} \delta(u)\,du = 1 \qquad (2.17)$$

A consequence of these two properties is that $\delta(u)$ must be infinite at $u = 0$. The delta function is normally represented graphically as shown in Figure 2.9(a), and can be visualized as the pulse illustrated in Figure 2.9(b) where τ becomes infinitesimally small and consequently $1/\tau$ becomes infinitely large. Replacing u by $u - u_0$, causes $\delta(u)$ to be shifted along the u axis and Figure 2.9(c) illustrates a commonly adopted way of representing $\delta(u - u_0)$

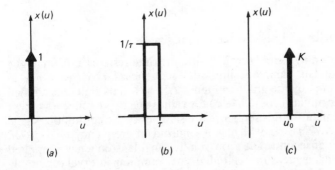

Figure 2.9 Dirac delta function (a) $x(u) = \delta(u)$ (b) approximation to $\delta(u)$ (c) $x(u) = K\delta(u - u_0)$

multiplied by a constant K. Variable u is generally replaced by either Ω or t, and $\delta(t)$ is commonly referred to as an 'impulse'. Assume now that a signal $x(t)$ has Fourier transform:

$$X(j\Omega) = 2\pi\delta(\Omega - \Omega_0) \qquad (2.18)$$

where Ω_0 is some fixed frequency. By Equation (2.16), $X(j\Omega) = 0$ for all values of Ω not equal to Ω_0 and by the inverse Fourier transform (Equation (2.11)):

$$x(t) = \frac{1}{2\pi} \int_{-\infty}^{\infty} 2\pi\delta(\Omega - \Omega_0)\, e^{j\Omega t}\, d\Omega$$

$$= \int_{-\infty}^{\infty} \delta(\Omega - \Omega_0)\, e^{j\Omega_0 t}\, d\Omega = e^{j\Omega_0 t} \int_{-\infty}^{\infty} \delta(\Omega - \Omega_0)\, d\Omega$$

$$(2.19)$$

$$= e^{j\Omega_0 t}$$

by Equation (2.17). Hence the inverse Fourier transform of $2\pi\delta(\Omega - \Omega_0)$ is $e^{j\Omega_0 t}$ which is a periodic signal with Fourier transform as yet undefined. We therefore define the Fourier transform of $e^{j\Omega_0 t}$ as $2\pi\delta(\Omega - \Omega_0)$. It follows that since:

$$\cos(\Omega_0 t + \phi) = \tfrac{1}{2}e^{j(\Omega_0 t + \phi)} + \tfrac{1}{2}e^{-j(\Omega_0 t + \phi)} \qquad (2.20)$$

the Fourier transform of $x(t) = A\cos(\Omega_0 t + \phi)$ becomes:

$$X(j\Omega) = \pi A e^{j\phi}\,\delta(\Omega + \Omega_0) + \pi A e^{-j\phi}\delta(\Omega - \Omega_0) \qquad (2.21)$$

All periodic signals which can be represented as Fourier series may now be Fourier transformed by adding together the expressions obtained for each harmonic.

2.3 Fourier analysis of discrete time signals

Sinusoids play a similar role in discrete time systems as in analogue systems. The sampled sinusoidal sequence $\{A\cos(\omega n + \phi)\}$ as represented by the graph in Figure 2.10 has all its elements defined by the formula $A\cos(\omega n + \phi)$ for values of n in the range $-\infty$ to ∞. The elements of this sequence are samples of the continuous signal $A\cos((\omega/T)t + \phi)$ which is a sinusoid of frequency ω/T or ωf_s radians per second. The term 'relative angular frequency' is applied to ω which is measured in radians per sampling interval (or simply 'per sample'). To convert ω to true frequency in radians per second, multiply by the sampling frequency f_s in samples per second

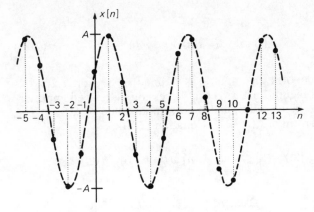

Figure 2.10 Sampled sinusoidal cos $(\omega n + \phi)$ with $\omega = 1.1$, $\phi = -\pi/3$

(Hertz). Table 2.1 lists commonly encountered values of ω with their corresponding true frequencies.

An important observation is that the sinusoidal sequences $\{\cos(\omega n)\}$ and $\{\cos[(\omega + 2\pi)n]\}$ cannot be distingushed since n is always an integer. Hence sampling the continuous signal $A\cos(((\omega + 2\pi)/T)t + \phi)$ produces the same sequence as would be produced by sampling $A\cos((\omega/T)t + \phi)$. The main consequences of this observation will be seen later. It is sufficient at this stage to note that restricting ω to the range 0 to 2π, or equivalently $-\pi$ to $+\pi$, would not result in any loss of generality.

Table 2.1

Relative frequency (radians/sample)	True frequency	
	(radians/sec)	(Hertz)
0	0	0
$\pi/6$	$\pi f_s/6$	$f_s/12$
$\pi/4$	$\pi f_s/4$	$f_s/8$
$\pi/3$	$\pi f_s/3$	$f_s/6$
$\pi/2$	$\pi f_s/2$	$f_s/4$
π	πf_s	$f_s/2$

2.3.1 Discrete time Fourier transform

Let $\{x[n]\}$ be a discrete time signal obtained by sampling the analogue signal $x_a(t)$ at intervals of T seconds. Define a new analogue signal:

$$x_s(t) = \sum_{n=-\infty}^{\infty} x[n]\,\delta(t - nT) \qquad (2.22)$$

where $\delta(t)$ denotes an impulse as defined in Section 2.2.4. As illustrated in Figure 2.11, $x_s(t)$ is a succession of delayed impulses, each impulse being multiplied by a sample value of $\{x[n]\}$. The Fourier transform of $x_s(t)$ is, by Equation (2.10):

$$X_s(j\Omega) = \int_{-\infty}^{\infty} \sum_{n=-\infty}^{\infty} x[n]\,\delta(t - nT)\,e^{-j\Omega t}\,dt$$

$$= \sum_{n=-\infty}^{\infty} x[n] \int_{-\infty}^{\infty} \delta(t - nT)\,e^{-j\Omega t}\,dt$$

$$= \sum_{n=-\infty}^{\infty} x[n]\,e^{-j\Omega nT} \qquad (2.23)$$

using the properties of $\delta(t)$ defined by Equations (2.16) and (2.17). Replacing Ω by $\omega f_s = \omega/T$ where ω denotes relative frequency, Equation (2.23) defines the discrete time Fourier transform (DTFT) of $\{x[n]\}$. It is denoted by $X(e^{j\omega})$ for reasons which will become clear later. Hence:

$$X(e^{j\omega}) = \sum_{n=-\infty}^{\infty} x[n]\,e^{-j\omega n} \qquad \text{(DTFT)} \quad (2.24)$$

and

$$X_s(j\Omega) = X(e^{j\omega}) \quad \text{with} \quad \omega = \Omega T. \qquad (2.25)$$

To understand why the DTFT is defined in this way the relationship between $X_s(j\Omega)$ and the Fourier transform $X_a(j\Omega)$ of

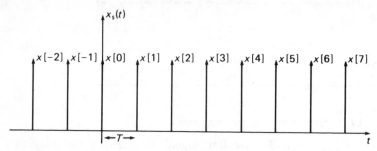

Figure 2.11 Succession of weighted and delayed analogue impulses

$x_a(t)$ must be explored. Since $x[n] = x_a(nT)$ for all values of n, Equation (2.22) can be rewritten as:

$$x_s(t) = \sum_{n=-\infty}^{\infty} x_a(t)\,\delta(t - nT) \tag{2.26}$$

$$= x_a(t)\,s(t) \tag{2.27}$$

where:

$$s(t) = \sum_{n=-\infty}^{\infty} \delta(t - nT) \tag{2.28}$$

Equation (2.28) defines a periodic function $s(t)$ which may be shown (see Problem (2.11)) to have the complex Fourier series:

$$s(t) = \frac{1}{T} \sum_{n=-\infty}^{\infty} e^{jn\Omega_0 t} \quad \text{where } \Omega_0 = 2\pi/T \tag{2.29}$$

Therefore, by Equation (2.10):

$$X_s(j\Omega) = \int_{-\infty}^{\infty} \left(x_a(t)\, \frac{1}{T} \sum_{n=-\infty}^{\infty} e^{jn\Omega_0 t} \right) e^{-j\Omega t}\, dt$$

$$= \frac{1}{T} \int_{-\infty}^{\infty} \sum_{n=-\infty}^{\infty} x_a(t)\, e^{-j(\Omega - n\Omega_0)t}\, dt$$

$$= \frac{1}{T} \sum_{n=-\infty}^{\infty} X_a(j(\Omega - n\Omega_0)) \quad \text{with } \Omega_0 = 2\pi/T \tag{2.30}$$

where $X_a(j\Omega)$ denotes the Fourier transform of $x_a(t)$. This equation shows that $X_s(j\Omega)$ is equal to the sum of an infinite number of identical copies of $X_a(j\Omega)$ each scaled by $1/T$ and shifted up or down in frequency by a multiple of $2\pi/T$ radians per second, i.e.:

$$X_s(j\Omega) = \frac{1}{T} X_a(j\Omega) + \frac{1}{T} X_a(j(\Omega - 2\pi/T))$$

$$+ \frac{1}{T} X_a(j(\Omega + 2\pi/T)) + \ldots \tag{2.31}$$

Equation (2.31) is valid for any analogue signal $x_a(t)$. For an analogue signal $x_a(t)$ which is bandlimited to a frequency range below π/T radians/second ($f_s/2$ Hertz), $X_a(j\Omega)$ is zero for all values of Ω with $|\Omega| \geq \pi/T$. It follows that:

$$X_s(j\Omega) = \frac{1}{T} X_a(j\Omega) \quad \text{for } \frac{-\pi}{T} < \Omega < \frac{\pi}{T} \tag{2.32}$$

and by Equation (2.25) the properties of $X(e^{j\omega})$ may be deduced from those of $X_s(j\Omega)$ by making ω equal to ΩT. These properties are now summarized.

(1) If $\{x[n]\}$ is obtained by sampling $x_a(t)$ which is bandlimited to $\pm f_s/2$ Hz, at f_s samples per second then:

$$X(e^{j\omega}) = \frac{1}{T}X_a(j\Omega) \quad \text{for } -\pi < \omega = \Omega T < \pi \qquad (2.33)$$

where $X_a(j\Omega)$ denotes the Fourier transform of $x_a(t)$ and $T = 1/f_s$. Hence $X(e^{j\omega})$ is closely related to the analogue frequency spectrum of $x_a(t)$ and is therefore referred to as the 'spectrum' of the digital signal $\{x[n]\}$.

(2) $X(e^{j\omega})$ is the Fourier transform of an analogue signal $x_s(t)$ consisting of a succession of impulses at intervals of $T = 1/f_s$ seconds multiplied by the corresponding elements of $\{x[n]\}$

(3) $X(e^{j\omega})$ is periodic in the sense that:

$$X(e^{j(\omega + 2\pi n)}) = X(e^{j\omega}) \qquad \text{for } n = 0, \pm 1, \pm 2, \dots \quad (2.34)$$

i.e. the relative frequency spectrum repeats at intervals of 2π.

(4) For real signals, $X(e^{-j\omega})$ is equal to the complex conjugate of $X(e^{j\omega})$.

2.3.2 *Inverse DTFT*

The elements of a sequence $\{x[n]\}$ may be expressed in terms of its spectrum $X(e^{j\omega})$ by an inverse DTFT formula derived from the inverse Fourier transform (2.11). Assuming that $\{x[n]\}$ is obtained by sampling $x_a(t)$ which is bandlimited to $\pm \pi/T$ radians/second:

$$x[n] = x_a[nT] = \frac{1}{2\pi} \int_{-\infty}^{\infty} X_a(j\Omega)\, e^{j\Omega nT}\, d\Omega \qquad \text{by Equation (2.15)}$$

$$= \frac{1}{2\pi} \int_{-\pi}^{\pi} TX(e^{j\omega})\, e^{j\omega n}\, d\omega/T$$

Therefore:

$$x[n] = \frac{1}{2\pi} \int_{-\pi}^{\pi} X(e^{j\omega})\, e^{j\omega n} d\omega \qquad \text{(inverse DTFT)} \quad (2.35)$$

2.4 Introduction to the discrete Fourier transform (DFT)

There are many applications of signal processing where it is useful to compute the spectrum of an analogue or digital signal by means of a computer program or special-purpose hardware. The DTFT can provide a convenient way of doing this since it involves summation rather than integration and produces a scaled version of the analogue Fourier transform of a suitably bandlimited signal. There are, however, two practical difficulties: first, the infinite range of summation and second, the fact that $X(e^{j\omega})$ is a continuous function of ω. The first difficulty is overcome by setting to zero all but a finite block of say N samples of $\{x[n]\}$ to produce the 'windowed' sequence $\{\ldots 0, \ldots, x[0], x[1], \ldots, x[N-1], 0, \ldots, 0, \ldots\}$. This infinite sequence may be conveniently represented by the finite sequence:

$$\{x[0], x[1], x[2], \ldots, x[N-1]\} \tag{2.36}$$

which will be denoted by $\{x[n]\}_{0,N-1}$. The second difficulty means that 'frequency domain sampling' must be used to obtain a representation of $X(e^{j\omega})$ as a finite set of complex numbers that can be stored in a computer. For real signals, it would be sufficient to store values of $X(e^{j\omega})$ only in the range $0 \leqslant \omega < \pi$ since $X(e^{-j\omega})$ is the complex conjugate of $X(e^{j\omega})$ and $X(e^{j\omega})$ is repetitive at intervals of 2π. In practice this range is often extended to $0 \leqslant \omega < 2\pi$ to allow for complex valued signals generated by mathematical formulae. Taking M equally spaced frequency domain samples in the range $0 \leqslant \omega < 2\pi$ produces the finite sequence of complex numbers:

$$\{X(e^{j\omega_k})\}_{0,M-1} = \{X(e^{j\omega_0}), X(e^{j\omega_1}), \ldots, X(e^{j\omega_{M-1}})\} \tag{2.37}$$

where:

$$\omega_k = 2\pi k/M \text{ for } k = 0, 1, \ldots, M-1. \tag{2.38}$$

For real signals, $X(e^{j(2\pi - \omega_k)})$ will be equal to the complex conjugate of $X(e^{j\omega_k})$ for all ω_k because the spectrum for $-\pi \leqslant \omega_k \leqslant 0$ is repeated for $\pi \leqslant \omega_k \leqslant 2\pi$.

The imposition of windowing and frequency domain sampling on the DTFT (Equation (2.24)) produces the following equation:

$$X(e^{j\omega_k}) = \sum_{n=0}^{N-1} x[n] e^{-j\omega_k n} \quad \text{where } \omega_k = 2\pi k/M \tag{2.39}$$

which is normally evaluated for $k = 0, 1, 2, \ldots, M-1$. For spectral analysis, the larger M is made, the easier it is to draw a smooth and accurate graph of the modulus and phase of $X(e^{j\omega})$ over the range $0 \leqslant \omega < 2\pi$. However in many applications it is important to evaluate just sufficient frequency domain samples to obtain a compact and unambiguous spectral representation of a windowed signal as quickly as possible. Multiplying Equation (2.39) by $e^{j\omega_k m}$

and summing over the block of M frequency domain samples:

$$\sum_{k=0}^{M-1} X(e^{j\omega_k}) e^{j\omega_k m} = \sum_{k=0}^{M-1} \sum_{n=0}^{N-1} x[n] e^{j\omega_k(m-n)}$$

$$= \sum_{n=0}^{N-1} x[n] \sum_{k=0}^{M-1} e^{2j\pi k(m-n)/M}$$

$$= Mx[m] \quad \text{if } 0 \leqslant m < N \text{ and } N \leqslant M$$

(2.40)

since it may be shown by summing the geometric series that provided $-M < m - n < M$:

$$\sum_{k=0}^{M-1} e^{2j\pi k(m-n)/M} = \begin{cases} M : \text{if } m = n \\ 0 : \text{if } m \neq n \end{cases}$$

(2.41)

The restriction $N \leqslant M$ is needed to ensure that $-M < m - n < M$ for all values of m and n in the range 0 to N. Relaxing this restriction would invalidate Equation (2.40) for some values of m.

Therefore, a minimum of N frequency domain samples are needed in the range $0 \leqslant \omega < 2\pi$ to ensure that all samples of $\{x[n]\}_{0,N-1}$ can be reconstructed exactly thus guaranteeing that no information about $\{x[n]\}_{0,N-1}$ is lost in the frequency domain sampling process. When $M = N$, the complex sequence defined by Equation (2.39) becomes the discrete Fourier transform (DFT) of $\{x[n]\}_{0,N-1}$. Introducing the following notation:

$$X(e^{j\omega_k}) = X[k]$$

(2.42)

the DFT may be defined as the transformation:

$$\{x[n]\}_{1,N-1} \xrightarrow{\text{DFT}} \{X[k]\}_{1,N-1}$$

(2.43)

with

$$X[k] = \sum_{n=0}^{N-1} x[n] e^{-j\omega_k n} \qquad \text{(DFT)}$$

(2.44)

and

$$\omega_k = 2\pi k/N \text{ for } k = 0, 1, 2, \ldots, N-1$$

(2.45)

It is normal to consider $\{x[n]\}_{0,N-1}$ as a complex sequence although its sample values may be given zero imaginary parts for real signals. The difference between the DFT and DTFT must be emphasised. The DFT transforms one finite sequence to another finite sequence whereas the DTFT transforms an essentially infinite sequence to a continuous function of ω. The following inverse DFT formula is obtained from Equation (2.40) with $M = N$:

$$\{x[k]\}_{0,N-1} \xrightarrow{\text{IDFT}} \{X[n]\}_{0,N-1} \qquad (2.46)$$

with

$$x[n] = \frac{1}{N} \sum_{k=0}^{N-1} X[k]\, e^{jn\omega_k} \qquad \text{(IDFT)} \qquad (2.47)$$

and ω_k defined as for the DFT.

The similarity between Equations (2.44) and (2.47) is exploited by readily available computer programs and hardware which are able to perform the DFT or its inverse using essentially the same code. Program 2.2 is presented for implementing the DFT and its inverse in a simple form. The DFT has many applications including the spectral analysis of analogue and digital signals in instrumentation systems such as spectrum analysers. Although the effect of windowing means that the DFT normally produces an approximation to the true Fourier transform of an infinite duration signal, the nature of this approximation is well understood and does not diminish the usefulness of the technique. The DFT is so important that a whole chapter (Chapter 6) is devoted to its efficient implementation and some of its applications.

Program 2.2 DDFT: direct DFT test program

```
10    REM DDFT .. DIRECT DFT
20    DIM X(31),XR(31),XI(31),YR(31),YI(31)
30    DEF FNR(A) = INT(A*1000+0.5)/1000
40    PRINT"NO. OF TIME OR FREQ SAMPLES"; : INPUT NS
50    PRINT"REAL PART OF INPUT :-"
60    GOSUB 10000
70    FOR N=0 TO NS-1 : XR(N)=X(N) : NEXT N
80    PRINT"IMAG PART OF INPUT :-"
90    GOSUB 10000
100   FOR N=0 TO NS-1 : XI(N)=X(N) : NEXT N
110   PRINT"ENTER D FOR DFT OR I FOR IDFT:"; : INPUT T$
120   GOSUB 200 : REM PERFORM DFT OR IDFT
130   PRINT"TRANSFORMED SEQUENCE IS:-"
140   PRINT" INDEX K"," REAL PT"," IMAG PT"
150   FOR K=0 TO NS-1
160     PRINT K,FNR(YR(K)),FNR(YI(K))
170   NEXT K
180   END
190   REM-----------------------------
200   REM SUBROUTINE FOR DFT OR IDFT
210   REM ORDER=NS, INPUT RE=XR(),IM=XI()
220   REM           OUTPUT RE=YR(),IM=YI()
```

```
230    REM  T$="D" FOR DFT,"I" FOR IDFT
240    IF T$="D" THEN PRINT"PERFORMING DFT"
250    E=8*ATN(1)/NS : REM 2*PI/NS
260    IF T$="I" THEN E=-E
270    FOR K=0 TO NS-1
280      YR(K)=0 : YI(K)=0 : WK=K*E
290      FOR N=0 TO NS-1
300        C=COS(N*WK) : S=SIN(N*WK)
310        YR(K)=YR(K)+XR(N)*C+XI(N)*S
320        YI(K)=YI(K)+XI(N)*C-XR(N)*S
330      NEXT N
340      IF T$="I" THEN YR(K)=YR(K)/NS
350      IF T$="I" THEN YI(K)=YI(K)/NS
360    NEXT K
370    RETURN
10000 REM --ARRAY DEFN. SUBROUTINE--
      (Listing as in Program 1.4 - see Chapter 1)
```

Sample run

```
NO. OF TIME OR FREQ SAMPLES:? 32
REAL PART OF INPUT:-
SEQUENCE TYPE ? SN
PERIODS OVER 32 SAMPLES ? 3
NO. OF SAMPLES DELAY ? 0
IMAG PART OF INPUT:-
SEQUENCE TYPE ? ZE
ENTER D FOR DFT OR I FOR IDFT:? D
PERFORMING DFT
TRANSFORMED SEQUENCE IS:-
```

INDEX K	REAL PT	IMAG PT
0	0	0
1	0	0
2	0	0
3	0	-16
4	0	0
5	0	0
:	:	:
28	0	0
29	0	16
30	0	0
31	0	0

Program notes

(1) Subroutine 10000 is used to place real and imaginary parts of the required input sequence in arrays XR and XI. The DFT/IDFT subroutine places the real and imaginary parts of the transformed sequence in arrays YR and YI.

(2) The sample run analyses a 32 sample segment of a sine wave with amplitude one. The segment contains three complete cycles, therefore the frequency of the sine wave is 3/32 times the sampling frequency. Its relative frequency is $\omega_0 = 3\pi/16$. The DTFT of $\{\sin(\omega_0 n)\}$ with ω restricted to $-\pi \leqslant \omega \leqslant \pi$ would be

$-\pi j\delta(\omega - \omega_0) + \pi j\delta(\omega + \omega_0)$, i.e. the sum of two weighted Dirac delta functions centered at $\omega = \omega_0$ respectively, and since the spectrum for $-\pi \leqslant \omega_k \leqslant 0$ and $\omega = -\omega_0$ is repeated for $\pi \leqslant \omega_k \leqslant 2\pi$, the weighted Dirac delta function $\pi j\delta(\omega + \omega_0)$ centered at $\omega = -\omega_0$ would appear also as $\pi j\delta(\omega - (2\pi - \omega_0))$ centred at $\omega = 2\pi - \omega_0$. The effect of windowing the sequence to a 32-sample segment has been to make the amplitude spectral density finite at $K = 3$ and $K = 29$, corresponding to ω_0 and $2\pi - \omega_0$ respectively.

(3) This direct program for the DFT has many calculations to perform and is therefore very slow. It is possible to speed up the program by the use of fast Fourier transform techniques which will be discussed in Chapter 6.

2.5 Signal energy and power

Familiar concepts such as intensity, volume and loudness are given mathematical expression by defining energy and power for signals. The energy of an analogue signal $x_a(t)$ is defined as the energy in joules that would be dissipated in a one ohm resistor when a voltage $x_a(t)$ is applied across it. It may be calculated by integrating $|x_a(t)|^2$ over $t = -\infty$ to $+\infty$ as indicated in Table 2.2, or by integrating the energy spectral density $(1/2\pi)|X_a(j\Omega)|^2$ over $\Omega = -\infty$ to $+\infty$. Parseval's theorem (see References 1–3) shows that these two formulae give the same result. A formula for the average power of $x_a(t)$ is also given in Table 2.2, this being defined as the average power in watts that would be dissipated by a one ohm resistor with a voltage $x_a(t)$ applied. For a signal with finite energy, the average power will always be zero, and signals with finite power, such as sinusoids for example, will have infinite energy.

Analogue concepts of energy and power may be extended to discrete time signals as indicated in Table 2.2. The energy of a sequence is the sum of its samples squared, and its power is the average value of its samples squared, i.e. its 'mean square value'. A discrete time version of Parseval's theorem (References 1–3) shows that energy may be calculated from the energy spectral density function $(1/2\pi)|X(e^{j\omega})|^2$ by the formula given in Table 2.2.

Analogue and discrete time concepts of energy and power are related in that if $\{x[n]\}$ is derived from a bandlimited signal $x_a(t)$ by sampling at a frequency f_s higher than twice its highest frequency component, the same value of power will be obtained for $\{x[n]\}$ as for $x_a(t)$, and the energy of $\{x[n]\}$ will be that of $x_a(t)$ multiplied by f_s. Analogue and discrete time definitions of energy spectral density

Table 2.2

	$x_a(t)$	$\{x[n]\}$
Energy	$\displaystyle\int_{-\infty}^{\infty} \mid x_a(t)\mid^2 dt$	$\displaystyle\sum_{n=-\infty}^{\infty} \mid x[n]\mid^2$
	$\displaystyle= \frac{1}{2\pi} \int_{-\infty}^{\infty} \mid X_a(j\Omega)\mid^2 d\Omega$	$\displaystyle= \frac{1}{2\pi} \int_{-\pi}^{\pi} \mid X(e^{j\omega})\mid^2 d\omega$
Average power	$\displaystyle\lim_{\tau\to\infty} \frac{1}{2\tau} \int_{-\tau}^{\tau} \mid x_a(t)\mid^2 dt$	$\displaystyle\lim_{M\to\infty} \frac{1}{2M+1} \sum_{n=-M}^{M} \mid x[n]\mid^2$

are also related, and the DFT is often employed for estimating the spectral distribution of energy or power in sampled analogue signals.

2.6 References

1. Lynn, P. A. (1982) *An introduction to the Analysis and Processing of Signals*, 2 ed, Macmillan
2. Papoulis, A. (1983) *Circuits and Systems A Modern Approach*, Holt, Rinehart and Winston
3. Meade, M. L. and Dillon, C. R. (1986) *Signals and Systems*, Van Nostrand Reinhold
4. Brigham, E. O. (1974) *The Fast Fourier Transform*, Prentice-Hall

Problems

(2.1) What is the phase of the sinusoid in Figure 2.3? Is it (a) $\pi/3$, (b) $2\pi/3$, or (c) $-\pi/3$?

(2.2) Re-express the Fourier series (2.7) as a complex Fourier series.

(2.3) Run Program 2.1 for the first ten harmonics of the Fourier series (2.8) with $\Omega = 1$ radian/second. Sketch the output, which represents a bandlimited square wave.

(2.4) The following infinite Fourier series represent commonly encountered periodic waveforms each of period 2π seconds. Run Program 2.1 for a truncated version of each of these series and try to decide what shape of waveform the infinite series represents

(a) $\cos(t) + (1/9)\cos(3t) + (1/25)\cos 5t + (1/49)\cos 7t$
      $+ (1/81)\cos 9t + \ldots$

(b) $\cos(t - \pi/2) - (4/3\pi)\cos 2t - (4/15\pi)\cos 4t - (4/35\pi)\cos 6t$
$\quad - (4/63\pi)\cos 8t - (4/99\pi)\cos 10t + \ldots$

(c) Waveform (b) with the fundamental component $(\cos(t - \pi/2))$ removed.

(d) $\cos t + \cos 2t + \cos 3t + \cos 4t + \ldots$

(2.5) The complex Fourier series coefficient c_n for a periodic waveform $x(t)$ of period P may be obtained by means of the following formula (References 1, 2):

$$c_n = \frac{1}{P} \int_{-P/2}^{P/2} x(t)\,e^{-jn\Omega_0 t}\,dt \quad \text{for } n = 0, \pm 1, \pm 2, \ldots \qquad (2.48)$$

Using this formula, show that for the ideal square wave illustrated in Figure 2.5, $c_0 = 1/2$ and $c_n = (1/\pi n)\sin(n\pi/2)$ when $n \neq 0$. Hence evaluate coefficients A_n and ϕ_n for the Fourier series noting that, by Equation (2.6), $A_n = 2c_n$ and $\phi_n = \arg(c_n)$. Confirm that the Fourier series (2.8) is obtained.

(2.6) Run Program 2.1 to estimate the effect on the shape of the bandlimited square wave analysed in Problem 2.3 of changing the phase of each sinusoidal component without affecting its frequency or amplitude. Consider two cases (a) where the phase of each component is increased by $\pi/2$ radians and (b) where the phase of each component is increased by three times its frequency i.e. $\cos(\Omega t)$ becomes $\cos(\Omega t + 3\Omega)$ for each value of Ω.

(2.7) Given that the Fourier transform of $x(t)$ is $X(j\Omega)$ show that the Fourier transform of $x(t - k)$ is $e^{-j\Omega k}\,X(j\Omega)$.

(2.8) A signal $x(t)$ has the Fourier transform

$$X(j\Omega) = \begin{cases} \pi & : \quad -1 \leqslant \Omega \leqslant 1 \text{ radians/second} \\ 0 & : \quad \text{otherwise} \end{cases}$$

Using the inverse Fourier transform (2.11) show that $x(t) = \mathrm{sinc}(t)$ where the 'sinc' function is as defined by Equation (2.15). Sketch the waveform $x(t)$.

(2.9) The signal $x_a(t) = \mathrm{sinc}(t)$ is sampled at 10 Hz to produce a sequence $\{x[n]\}$. Show that the DTFT of $\{x[n]\}$ is

$$X(e^{j\omega}) = \begin{cases} 10\pi & : \quad -0.1 \leqslant \omega \leqslant 0.1 \text{ radians/sample} \\ 0 & : \quad 0.1 < |\omega| < \pi \end{cases}$$

(2.10) A sinusoid of frequency 1 kHz is sampled at 10 kHz. What is the relative frequency of the resulting sinusoidal sequence?

(2.11) Using the two properties of $\delta(t)$ defined by Equations (2.16) and (2.17), show that $s(t)$ as defined by Equation (2.28) has the complex Fourier series (2.34).

(2.12) Calculate the energy of $x_a(t) = \text{sinc}\,(t)$ and show that its average power is zero. Show that the energy of $\{x[n]\}$ as obtained by sampling $x_a(t)$ at 10 Hz is equal to ten times the energy of $x_a(t)$. Hint: Use frequency domain formulae and refer to Problems 2.8 and 2.9.

(2.13) Show that the average power of $A\cos(\Omega t + \phi)$ is $A^2/2$ for any nonzero value of Ω, and that average power of $\{A\cos(\omega n + \phi)\}$ is $A^2/2$ for any value of ω in the range $0 < \omega < \pi$.

(2.14) Run Program 2.2 to calculate the 32-point DFT of a segment of $\{\cos((7\pi/32)n)\}$. Note that $7\pi/32$ radians/sample does not coincide with a frequency sampling point, and lies between $3\pi/16$ ($k = 3$) and $\pi/4$ ($k = 4$). Plot the amplitude spectral density against frequency and observe the effect of 'frequency spreading' [1–3]. Why was frequency spreading not apparent in the sample run for Program 2.2?

Chapter 3
Digital signal processing

3.1 Introduction

A digital signal processing system with input signal $\{x[n]\}$ and output signal $\{y[n]\}$ is often shown as a 'black box' as illustrated in Figure 3.1. The black box typically represents a general purpose computer, a microcomputer or a dedicated piece of digital hardware

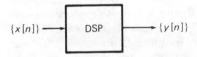

Figure 3.1 Digital signal processing system

which is capable of carrying out arithmetic operations on the samples of $\{x[n]\}$ and $\{y[n]\}$. An endless variety of processes could be considered. For example, suppose the digital system were required to produce an output sequence $\{y[n]\}$ with:

$$y[n] = 0.2(x[n] + x[n-1] + x[n-2] + x[n-3] + x[n-4]) \qquad (3.1)$$

for all values of n. The system would supply, at time n, the average of five consecutive samples of $\{x[n]\}$ up to and including the current sample and could be used to smooth out uncertainties in measurements of some fixed or slowly varying quantity. It could be conceived as a microcomputer running Program 3.1 as listed below.

Program 3.1 AVGE: five point average

```
10 REM AVGE .. FIVE PT AVERAGE
20 X1=0 : X2=0 : X3=0 : X4=0
30 FOR N=0 TO 9
40 PRINT"X(";N;")":"; : INPUT X
50 Y=(X+X1+X2+X3+X4)/5
60 PRINT"Y(";N") =";Y
70 X4=X3 : X3=X2 : X2=X1 : X1=X
80 NEXT N
90 END
```

35

```
Sample  run

X(0):? 5                 Y(0)=1
X(1):? 5                 Y(1)=2
X(2):? 10                Y(2)=4
X(3):? 5                 Y(3)=5
X(4):? 15                Y(4)=8
X(5):? 10                Y(5)=11
X(6):? 15                Y(6)=11
X(7):? 25                Y(7)=12
X(8):? 10                Y(8)=13
X(9):? 20                Y(9)=14
```

Program notes

(1) Input samples are entered on the keyboard and output samples are printed on the VDU. Ten input samples are expected, although a simple modification to statement 30 will allow the program to process any number of samples.

(2) The structure of this program is conveniently represented by the 'signal flow graph' shown in Figure 3.2. This graph consists of four delay elements labelled z^{-1} (for reasons that will become apparent in a later section), four summing elements with circular symbols, and a constant multiplier represented by a triangular symbol. The elements are connected by signal flow paths showing how their inputs are derived from appropriate outputs or in one case, the input signal. The output from the four delay elements are labelled X1, X2, X3 and X4 respectively and these correspond to BASIC variables used in the program. Thus input and output sequences appear at X and Y respectively which also have associated BASIC variables.

(3) As each input sample $x[n]$ is received, it is stored in X with the four previous input samples $x[n-1], x[n-2], x[n-3]$ and $x[n-4]$, held in X1, X2, X3 and X4 respectively. The sequence at X1 should therefore be the input sequence X delayed by one sample; the sequence at X2 should be X1 delayed by one sample and so on. This is achieved by shifting X3 into X4, X2 into X3, X1 into X2 and X

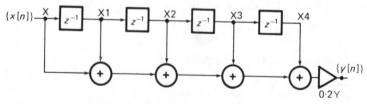

Figure 3.2 Signal flow graph for five-point averaging system

into X1 before each new input sample is read into X. Initially, X1, X2, X3 and X4 are set to zero on the assumption that all samples of $\{x[n]\}$ are zero for $n < 0$ and that the first input sample is received at $n = 0$. For each input sample a corresponding output sample is calculated as indicated by the signal flow graph and stored in Y.

(4) Note that only five BASIC variables are needed regardless of how many input samples are required to be processed. With a simple modification to the 'INPUT' statement, the program could be made to read from an array of stored sample values instead of from the keyboard. It is also conceivable that input samples could be taken directly from an analogue to digital converter, although the speed of BASIC would impose a very low sampling rate, typically less than 100 Hz.

(5) The sample run analyses a sequence of voltage measurements which, despite fluctuations due to experimental error, shows an underlying upward trend.

3.2 Further examples

Programs similar to Program 3.1 may be devised for any of the following formulae which exemplify processes commonly applied to digital signals:

$$y[n] = 0.1x[n] - 0.3x[n - 1] + 0.4x[n - 2]$$
$$- 0.3x[n - 3] + 0.1x[n - 4] \qquad (3.2)$$

$$y[n] = x[n] - x[n - 1] + 0.42y[n - 1] \qquad (3.3)$$

$$y[n] = 0.2x[n] - 0.2x[n - 5] + y[n - 1] \qquad (3.4)$$

$$y[n] = 0.2(x[n]^2 + x[n - 1]^2 + x[n - 2]^2$$
$$+ x[n - 3]^2 + x[n - 4]^2) \qquad (3.5)$$

$$y[n] = x[n] \cos(\pi n/3) \qquad (3.6)$$

Equation (3.2) may be implemented in BASIC by a slightly modified version of Program 3.1 (see Problem 3.1). A signal flow graph for the required program is given in Figure 3.3. Program 3.2

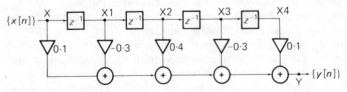

Figure 3.3 Signal flow graph for a fourth-order nonrecursive difference equation

below is an implementation of Equation (3.3) which expresses each output sample $y[n]$ in terms of the previously calculated output sample $y[n-1]$ as well as input samples $x[n]$ and $x[n-1]$. Equation (3.4) may be programmed in a similar manner to Equation (3.3) (see Problem 3.2) and Equations (3.5) and (3.6) may also be programmed and investigated without difficulty. Clearly, many similar formulae could be devised.

Program 3.2 RECUR: implementation of Equation (3.3)

```
10 REM  RECUR .. Y[N]=X[N]-X[N-1]+0.42*Y[N-1]
20 X1=0 : Y1=0
30 N=0
40 PRINT"X(";N;"):"; : INPUT X
50 Y=X-X1+0.42*Y1
60 PRINT"Y(";N;")=";Y
70 X1=X : Y1=Y
80 N=N+1 : GOTO 40
90 END
```

Sample run

X(0):? 5	Y(0)=5
X(1):? 5.707	Y(0)=2.807
X(2):? 6	Y(2)=1.472
X(3):? 5.707	Y(3)=0.325
X(4):? 5	Y(4)=-0.571
X(5):? 4.293	Y(5)=-0.941
X(6):? 4	Y(6)=-0.691
X(7):? 4.293	Y(7)=0.003
X(8):? 5	Y(8)=0.708
X(9):? 5.707	Y(9)=1.005
X(10):? 6	Y(10)=0.715
.	.

Program notes

(1) A signal flow graph for this program is shown in Figure 3.4 with Y1 denoting the sequence at Y delayed by one sample.

(2) This program runs until interrupted and hence is able to process as many input samples as may be required.

(3) For the sample run, a signal is input with value $5 + \sin(n\pi/4)$ at time nT for $n \geq 0$. It may be seen that the program separates $\sin(n\pi/4)$ from the constant 5 which is gradually removed. After about 10 samples the output sequence settles down to $\sin(n\pi/4)$ delayed by approximately seven samples.

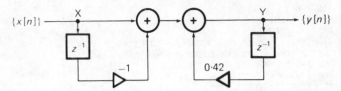

Figure 3.4 Signal flow graph for a first-order recursive difference equation

3.3 Digital filters

Equations (3.1) to (3.6) are referred to as 'difference equations' since the output is expressed in terms of sums and differences of functions of input and output samples. Difference equations (3.1), (3.2), (3.3) and (3.4) may be generalized to:

$$y[n] = \frac{1}{b_0}\left(\sum_{i=0}^{N} a_i x[n-i] - \sum_{j=1}^{M} b_j y[n-j] \right) \qquad (3.7)$$

where a_i and b_j are constants for all values of i and j, and $b_0 \neq 0$. A program which implements such a difference equation is said to be a 'digital filter', and it will be seen that digital filters are able to affect digital signals in much the same way as analogue filters affect analogue signals. The digital filter is said to be 'causal' and of 'order' N or M depending on which is greater. (Non-causal digital filters are sometimes discussed, e.g., see Reference [1], but cannot be implemented in real time.) When M is greater than zero, as in Equations (3.3) and (3.4), the difference equation is 'recursive' since previous values of $y[n]$ are used in calculating new outputs. When $M = 0$, as in Equation (3.1) and (3.2), the difference equation is 'non-recursive'. Equations (3.5) and (3.6) represent perfectly valid digital signal processing systems which are not classed as digital filters. Program 3.3 generalizes the two previous programs to implement Equation (3.7) with user selectable coefficients. A means of testing digital filters with various input waveforms as generated by 'subroutine 10000' (see Chapter 1) is incorporated into this program.

Program 3.3 GDFIL: general digital filter implementation

```
10REM  GDFIL ..   GENERAL DIGITAL FILTER
20 DIM A(50),B(3),X1(51),Y1(4),X(100)
30 PRINT"ENTER N:"; : INPUT NN
40 PRINT"ENTER M:"; : INPUT MM
50 FOR I=0 TO NN
60  PRINT"A";I;": "; : INPUT A(I)
70 NEXT I
```

```
 80 FOR J=0 TO MM
 90   PRINT"B";J;": "; : INPUT B(J)
100 NEXT J : PRINT"OK"
110 PRINT"TEST SEQUENCE LENGTH:"; : INPUT NS
120 GOSUB 10000 : REM GENERATE TEST SEQUENCE
130 FOR I=0 TO NN : X1(I)=0 : NEXT I
140 FOR J=0 TO MM : Y1(J)=0 : NEXT J
150 PRINT"START FILTERING:"
160 FOR N=0 TO NS-1
170 Y=A(0)*X(N)
180 IF NN=0 THEN GOTO 230
190 FOR I=0 TO NN-1
200   Y=Y+A(NN-I)*X1(NN-I)
210   X1(NN-I+1)=X1(NN-I)
220 NEXT I
230 IF MM=0 THEN GOTO 280
240 FOR J=0 TO MM-1
250   Y=Y-B(MM-J)*Y1(MM-J)
260   Y1(MM-J+1)=Y1(MM-J)
270 NEXT J
280 Y=Y/B(0) : Y1(1)=Y : X1(1)=X(N)
290 PRINT"X(";N;")=";X(N)," Y(";N;")=";Y
300 NEXT N
310 STOP
10000 REM ARRAY DEFN. SUBROUTINE
        Listing as for Program 1.4
```

Sample run

```
ENTER N:? 5
ENTER M:? 1
A0:? 0.2
A1:? 0
A2:? 0
A3:? 0
A4:? 0
A5:? -0.2
B0:? 1
B1:?-1
OK
TEST SEQUENCE LENGTH:? 10
SEQUENCE TYPE:?ME
START,END SAMPLE NO.:?0,9
VALUE NUMBER 0:? 5
VALUE NUMBER 1:? 5
VALUE NUMBER 2:? 10
VALUE NUMBER 3:? 5
VALUE NUMBER 4:? 15
VALUE NUMBER 5:? 10
VALUE NUMBER 6:? 15
VALUE NUMBER 7:? 25
VALUE NUMBER 8:? 10
VALUE NUMBER 9:? 20
START FILTERING:
X(0)=5   Y(0)=1
X(1)=5   Y(1)=2
X(2)=10  Y(2)=4
```

```
X(3)=5    Y(3)=5
X(4)=15   Y(4)=8
X(5)=10   Y(5)=9
   .         .
   .         .
   .         .
```

Program notes

(1) Nonrecursive filters of order up to fifty and recursive filters with $N \le 50$ and $M \le 3$ may be implemented. Restrictions on N and M (NN and MM in the program) are easily relaxed by modifying statement 20.

(2) The program is similar to the previous programs except that arrays instead of individual variables are used to store coefficients and previous signal values.

(3) The sample run gives the response of the recursive digital filter with difference Equation (3.4) to the same input sequence as was used to test Program 3.1. Note that the outputs produced are the same.

3.4 Linear time-invariant systems

When considering Equation (3.7) it is normal to assume that both input and output signals are zero up to some point in time, which may be at $n = 0$ or some other starting point very far back in time. In practice this is arranged by setting to zero all variables at the beginning of a digital filtering program and, if necessary, leaving the program to run for some time before observing the output sequence. Under these conditions, a digital filter can be shown to obey the principles of superposition (linearity) and time-invariance as defined below, and is therefore said to be a linear time invariant (LTI) system. Before defining superposition, it is necessary to introduce the following notation:

Notation: Given any two sequences $\{x_1[n]\}$ and $\{x_2[n]\}$ and any two constants k_1 and k_2, let $k_1\{x_1[n]\} + k_2\{x_2[n]\}$ denote the sequence $\{k_1 x_1[n] + k_2 x_2[n]\}$. This notation allows sequences to be multiplied by constants and added together on a sample-by-sample basis.

Superposition: If the system's response to input sequences $\{x_1[n]\}$ and $\{x_2[n]\}$ are denoted by $\{y_1[n]\}$ and $\{y_2[n]\}$ respectively then the response to $k_1\{x_1[n]\} + k_2\{x_2[n]\}$ is $k_1\{y_1[n]\} + k_2\{y_2[n]\}$ for any values of the constants k_1 and k_2. It may be inferred that the response to:

$$\sum_{i=-\infty}^{\infty} k_i\{x_i[n]\} \quad \text{is} \quad \sum_{i=-\infty}^{\infty} k_i\{y_i[n]\}$$

where $\{y_i[n]\}$ denotes the response to $\{x_i[n]\}$ for each value of i.

Time-invariance: (sometimes called 'shift-invariance'). If the system's response to an input $\{x[n]\}$ is $\{y[n]\}$ then the response to $\{x[n-N]\}$ will be $\{y[n-N]\}$ for any value of the integer N. This means that any delay introduced in the input sequence produces a corresponding delay in the output sequence.

Equations (3.1) to (3.4) are special cases of Equation (3.7) and therefore produce LTI systems. It may be shown that Equation (3.5) is time-invariant but non-linear and that Equation (3.6) is linear but not time-invariant.

3.5 Discrete time unit impulse

In studying an LTI system, it is useful to consider its response to a special digital signal referred to as a 'discrete-time unit impulse', or in short an 'impulse', denoted $\{d[n]\}$. This signal has only one non-zero sample as illustrated in Figure 3.5. The non-zero sample occurs at $n = 0$ and has value 1. Each sample of the sequence is defined by:

$$d[n] = \begin{cases} 1 : n = 0 \\ 0 : n \neq 0 \end{cases} \tag{3.8}$$

Note that $d[n]$ is not infinite at $n = 0$, and that a discrete-time 'impulse' is consequently easier to visualize than its analogue counterpart discussed in Section 2.2.3. Since, by Equation (3.8), $d[n-m]$ is zero except at $n = m$ where its value is 1, it follows that $\{d[n-m]\}$ is a delayed unit impulse whose non-zero value occurs

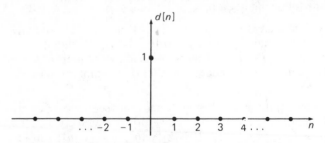

Figure 3.5 Discrete time unit impulse

at $n = m$. It also follows that for any element of a general sequence $\{x[n]\}$:

$$x[n] = \sum_{m=-\infty}^{\infty} x[m]\, d[n - m] \tag{3.9}$$

and hence that:

$$\{x[n]\} = \sum_{m=-\infty}^{\infty} x[m]\, \{d[n - m]\} \tag{3.10}$$

The sequence $\{x[n]\}$ has thus been expressed as the sum of an infinite number of delayed impulses $\{d[n - m]\}$ each multiplied by a single element $x[m]$ of the sequence.

3.5.1. Impulse response

When $\{d[n]\}$ is applied as the input to a digital LTI system, the output, $\{h[n]\}$ say, is termed the 'impulse response' of the system and is of great significance. The impulse response for any of the digital filters considered in Sections 3.1 and 3.2 may be obtained by running the appropriate BASIC program and entering samples of $\{d[n]\}$. Running Program 3.1 for Equation (3.2) produces the output sequence:

$$\{h[n]\} = \{\ldots, 0, \ldots, 0, 0.2, 0.2, 0.2, 0.2, 0.2, 0, \ldots, 0, \ldots\} \tag{3.11}$$

which is termed a 'finite impulse response' since the sequence is non-zero for only a finite number of samples. In general, the impulse response of a digital filter with the non-recursive difference equation:

$$y[n] = \sum_{i=0}^{N} a_i x[n - i] \tag{3.12}$$

is $\{h[n]\} = \{\ldots, 0, \ldots, 0, a_0, a_1, \ldots, a_N, 0, \ldots\}$ (3.13)

which is just the finite sequence of multiplier values starting at $n = 0$, preceded and followed by zero valued samples.

Running Program 3.2 for the recursive difference Equation (3.3) produces the following impulse response which in principle does not become zero no matter how many samples are considered:

$$\{h[n]\} = \{\ldots, 0, 1, -.58, -.24, -.10, -.043, -.018, -.0076, \ldots\}$$
$$\tag{3.14}$$

This is termed an 'infinite impulse response'. Not all recursive difference equations produce infinite impulse responses and Equation (3.4) produces the same finite impulse response (Equation (3.11)) as was obtained for Equation (3.1) (see Problem 3.2). Digital filters are divided into two types: finite impulse response (FIR) types and infinite impulse response (IIR) types. IIR filters require recursive difference equations, whereas FIR types may have either recursive or nonrecursive difference equations. Both types are commonly used and have particular advantages and disadvantages as will be seen in Chapter 5.

3.5.2 Stability and causality

An LTI system is said to be stable if its impulse response $\{h[n]\}$ satisfies:

$$\sum_{n=-\infty}^{\infty} |h[n]| \quad \text{is finite} \qquad \text{(stability condition)} \quad (3.15)$$

This means that $\{h[n]\}$ must either be a finite impulse response or it must decay towards zero as n tends to $\pm\infty$. If the system is causal, its impulse response $\{h[n]\}$ satisfies:

$$h[n] = 0 \text{ for } n < 0 \qquad \text{(causality condition)} \qquad (3.16)$$

which means that it cannot anticipate the non-zero sample of $\{d[n]\}$ at $n = 0$ by becoming nonzero for values of $n < 0$. Any practical LTI system operating in real time must be causal.

3.6 Discrete-time convolution

If the impulse response of an LTI system is $\{h[n]\}$, the system's response to a delayed impulse $\{d[n-m]\}$ is $\{h[n-m]\}$. The response to a general sequence $\{x[n]\}$ may be obtained by summing the responses to each of the terms in the infinite summation on the right hand side of Equation (3.10). Each of these terms is simply a delayed impulse multiplied by a constant. Therefore the response to $\{x[n]\}$ will be an output sequence:

$$\{y[n]\} = \sum_{m=-\infty}^{\infty} x[m]\{h[n-m]\} \qquad (3.17)$$

meaning that each element is given by the formula:

$$y[n] = \sum_{m=-\infty}^{\infty} x[m]\,h[n-m] \qquad \text{(convolution)} \quad (3.18)$$

Replacing $n - m$ by k in this formula gives an alternative expression which is entirely equivalent:

$$y[n] = \sum_{k=-\infty}^{\infty} h[k] x[n-k] \qquad \text{(convolution)} \qquad (3.19)$$

The sequence $\{y[n]\}$ whose elements are given by Equation (3.18), or equivalently Equation (3.19), is said to be the discrete-time convolution of sequences $\{x[n]\}$ and $\{h[n]\}$ denoted thus:

$$\{y[n]\} = \{x[n]\} \times \{h[n]\}$$

or equivalently:

$$\{y[n]\} = \{h[n]\} \times \{x[n]\}.$$

3.7 System function

Much can be learnt about the behaviour of a discrete-time LTI system by considering its response to the complex-valued input sequence:

$$\{x[n]\} = \{z^n\} \qquad (3.20)$$

$$= \{\ldots\ldots z^{-2}, z^{-1}, 1, z, z^2, \ldots\ldots\}$$

where z may be any complex number with modulus greater than or equal to 1. Writing z in polar form as:

$$z = R\, e^{j\omega} \qquad (3.21)$$

the sequence becomes:

$$\{z^n\} = \{R^n e^{j\omega n}\}$$

$$= \{R^n \cos(\omega n)\} + j\{R^n \sin(\omega n)\} \qquad (3.22)$$

Hence the real and imaginary parts of z^n form sinusoidal sequences of relative frequency ω as defined in Section 2.3, with amplitudes which increase exponentially as $n \to \infty$ when $R > 1$, or remain fixed at 1 when $R = 1$.

The response of a digital LTI system with impulse response $\{h[n]\}$ to an input sequence $\{z^n\}$ with $|z| \geqslant 1$ is, by the convolution formula (3.19):

$$\{y[n]\} = \left\{ \sum_{k=-\infty}^{\infty} h[k]\, z^{(n-k)} \right\}$$

$$= \left\{ z^n \sum_{k=-\infty}^{\infty} h[k]\, z^{-k} \right\}$$

$$= H(z)\,\{z^n\} \qquad (3.23)$$

where:

$$H(z) = \sum_{n=-\infty}^{\infty} h[n] z^{-n} \qquad (z\text{-transform of } \{h[n]\}) \quad (3.24)$$

The output sequence is the input sequence $\{z^n\}$ multiplied by $H(z)$ where $H(z)$ is defined by Equation (3.24) and is said to be the z-transform of $\{h[n]\}$. For a causal and stable system:

$$|H(z)| \leqslant \sum_{n=0}^{\infty} |h[n]| \, |z|^{-n} \leqslant \sum_{n=0}^{\infty} |h[n]| \quad (3.25)$$

where $|z| \geqslant 1$. By the stability condition (Equation (3.15)), $H(z)$ must therefore be finite for all values of z with $|z| \geqslant 1$.

Calculating $H(z)$ for an FIR or IIR digital filter is straightforward as will now be demonstrated. For an FIR digital filter with the general non-recursive difference Equation (3.12), the impulse response (3.13) is substituted into Equation (3.24) to obtain:

$$H(z) = \sum_{i=0}^{N} a_i z^{-i} \quad (3.26)$$

Hence for the FIR digital filter shown in Figure 3.2:

$$H(z) = 0.2 + 0.2z^{-1} + 0.2z^{-2} + 0.2z^{-3} + 0.2z^{-4} \quad (3.27)$$

For the IIR digital filter shown in Figure 3.3, with the infinite impulse response (3.17), Equation (3.24) becomes an infinite series of terms in z^{-1}:

$$H(z) = 1 - 0.58z^{-1} - 0.24z^{-2} - 0.1z^{-3} - 0.043z^{-4} + \ldots$$

which must converge when $|z| \geqslant 1$. Although a convenient expression for $H(z)$ may be calculated by summing the series, an indirect approach is much more convenient. Recall that the difference equation is:

$$y[n] = x[n] - x[n-1] + 0.42x[n-2]$$

and that an input sequence $\{z^n\}$ with $|z| \geqslant 1$ must produce the output sequence $H(z)\{z^n\}$ with $H(z)$ finite. Substituting $x[n] = z^n$ and $y[n] = H(z)z^n$ which means that $x[n-1] = z^{n-1}$ and $y[n-1] = H(z)z^{n-1}$, it follows that:

$$H(z)z^n = z^n - z^{n-1} + 0.42 H(z)z^{-1}$$

Therefore:

$$H(z) = \frac{z^n - z^{n-1}}{z^n - 0.42z^{n-1}} = \frac{1 - z^{-1}}{1 - 0.42z^{-1}} \quad (3.28)$$

since the demoninator is non-zero for all values of z with $|z| \geq 1$.

The previous example illustrates a technique that may also be used to derive $H(z)$ for a general causal and stable digital filter as defined by difference Equation (3.7). Substituting $x[n] = z^n$ and $y[n] = H(z)z^n$ with $|z| \geq 1$, the same technique gives:

$$H(z) = \frac{a_0 + a_1 z^{-1} + a_2 z^{-2} + \ldots + b_N z^{-N}}{b_0 + b_1 z^{-1} + b_2 z^{-2} + \ldots + b_M z^{-M}} \tag{3.29}$$

A nonzero denominator may be safely assumed since $H(z)$ must be finite whenever $|z| \geq 1$. Although the expression obtained above for $H(z)$ is guaranteed to be equal to the z-transform of the impulse response only when $|z| \geq 1$, it is useful to refer to it without any restrictions on z as the 'system function' or 'transfer function' of the digital filter. This is done on the understanding that when $|z| < 1$, any correspondence with the z-transform may be lost and that the expression may become infinite.

3.8 Frequency response

When $|z| = 1$, the sequence $\{z^n\}$ becomes, by Equation (3.22):

$$\{z^n\} = \{e^{j\omega n}\} = \{\cos(\omega n) + j\sin(\omega n)\}$$

and the response to such an input signal would be:

$$\{y[n]\} = H(e^{j\omega})\{e^{j\omega n}\} \tag{3.30}$$

where

$$H(e^{j\omega}) = \sum_{n=-\infty}^{\infty} h[n] e^{-j\omega n} \qquad \text{(frequency response)} \tag{3.31}$$

$H(e^{j\omega})$ is referred to as the 'relative frequency response' or, for short, the frequency response. Comparing Equations (3.31) and (2.24), it may be seen that $H(e^{j\omega})$ is identical to the discrete time Fourier transform (DTFT) of the impulse response $\{h[n]\}$. The stability criterion (3.15) ensures that this is finite. The modulus and phase of $H(e^{j\omega})$ determine the response to a sampled sinusoidal input of relative frequency ω as will now be shown. Let:

$$G(\omega) = |H(e^{j\omega})| \text{ and } \theta(\omega) = \arg(H(e^{j\omega})) \text{ in radians} \tag{3.32}$$

and refer to $G(\omega)$ and $\theta(\omega)$ as the gain response and phase response respectively. Where the impulse response $\{h[n]\}$ is real it follows from the properties of the DTFT established in Section 2.3.1 that $H(e^{-j\omega})$ is the complex conjugate of $H(e^{j\omega})$ and therefore:

$$G(-\omega) = G(\omega) \text{ and } \theta(-\omega) = -\theta(\omega) \tag{3.33}$$

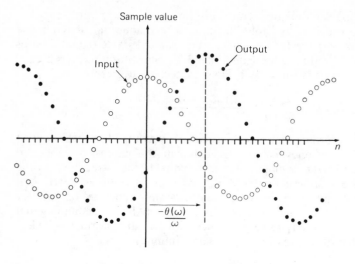

Figure 3.6 Response of LTI system to sampled sinusoid

Let the input signal be:

$$\{x[n]\} = \{A\cos(\omega n + \phi)\} \qquad (3.34)$$

which can be written as:

$$\{x[n]\} = \{(A/2)\,e^{j(\omega n + \phi)} + (A/2)\,e^{-j(\omega n + \phi)}\} \qquad (3.35)$$

$$= (A/2)\,e^{j\phi}\{e^{j\omega n}\} + (A/2)\,e^{-j\phi}\{e^{-j\omega n}\}$$

By Equation (3.30) the response will be:

$$\{y[n]\} = (A/2)e^{j\phi}\,H(e^{j\omega})\{e^{j\omega n}\} + (A/2)\,e^{-j\phi}\,H(e^{-j\omega})\{e^{-j\omega n}\}$$

$$= (A/2)\,G(\omega)\{e^{j(\phi+\theta(\omega)+\omega n)} + e^{-j(\phi+\theta(\omega)+\omega n)}\}$$

$$= \{AG(\omega)\cos(\omega n + \phi + \theta(\omega))\} \qquad (3.36)$$

The response is a sampled sinusoid of the same relative frequency as the input, but with amplitude mutliplied by $G(\omega)$ and phase increased by $\theta(\omega)$ radians as illustrated in Figure 3.6. The output leads the input by $\theta(\omega)$ radians and this means that the output is effectively delayed by $k = -\theta(\omega)/\omega$ sampling intervals with respect to the input as may be seen by re-expressing Equation (3.36) as:

$$\{y[n]\} = \{AG(\omega)\cos(\omega(n-k) + \phi)\} \qquad (3.37)$$

3.9 Gain and phase response graphs

It is common practice to plot graphs of the gain and phase responses $G(\omega)$ and $\theta(\omega)$ against ω. $G(\omega)$ is often converted to decibels (dBs) by calculating $20\log_{10}(G(\omega))$. Hence when $G(\omega) = 1$, the gain is 0 dB, and other gains are listed in Table 3.1 with their corresponding decibel values. Phase lag, $-\theta(\omega)$, is often plotted instead of phase lead $\theta(\omega)$ with $\theta(\omega)$ restricted to the range -2π to 0 radians or $-360°$ to $0°$. It is normally satisfactory to restrict ω in the range 0 to π (or 0 to 180°) with the knowledge that $G(-\omega) = G(\omega)$ and $\theta(-\omega) = -\theta(\omega)$ for real valued impulse responses. A linear scale can be used for ω.

Table 3.1

$G(\omega)$	Gain (approx. in dB.)
10	20
4	12
2	6
1.414	3
1	0
0.707	−3
0.5	−6
0.25	−12
0.1	−20
0.01	−40
0.001	−60

Plotting the gain and phase responses for FIR and IIR filters such as those shown in Figures 3.2, 3.3 and 3.4 requires an evaluation of $H(e^{j\omega})$ for a range of values of ω. Program 3.4 performs these evaluations for a general digital filter whose system function is given by Equation (3.29).

Program 3.4 HZAN: gain and phase response

```
 10 REM HZAN .. GAIN & PHASE RESP.
 20 DIM A(100), B(10)
 25 DEF FNR(X)=INT(X*1000+0.5)/1000
 30 PRINT"SAMPLING FREQ (HZ):"; : INPUT FS
 40 PRINT"NUMERATOR ORDER: "; : INPUT NN
 50 PRINT"DENOMINATOR ORDER:"; : INPUT MM
 60 PRINT"ENTER NUMERATOR COEFFS:-"
 70 FOR I = 0 TO NN
 80  PRINT "A";I;": "; : INPUT A(I)
 90 NEXT I : PRINT"OK"
100 PRINT"ENTER DENOMINATOR COEFFS:-"
110 FOR J=0 TO MM
```

```
120  PRINT"B";J;": "; : INPUT B(J)
130 NEXT J : PRINT"OK"
140 PRINT"ENTER INCREMENT(HZ): "; : INPUT FI
150 PRINT : F=0
160 PRINT"FREQUENCY","  GAIN","PHASE LEAD"
170 PRINT" (HERTZ) ","   (DB.)"," (DEGREES)"
180 W=6.283185308*F/FS :REM RELATIVE FREQ
190 R1=0 : I1=0 :REM REAL & IMAG PTS OF NUM
200 FOR I=0 TO NN
210  R1=R1+A(I)*COS(I*W)
220  I1=I1-A(I)*SIN(J*W)
230 NEXT I
240 R2=0 : I2=0 :REM REAL & IMAG PTS OF DEN
250 FOR J=0 TO MM
260  R2=R2+B(J)*COS(J*W)
270  I2=I2-B(J)*SIN(J*W)
280 NEXT J
290 GOSUB 600 : REM GET G & P
300 PRINT FNR(F),FNR(G),FNR(P*57.29578)
310 F=F+FI
320 IF F<FS/2+FI THEN GOTO 180
330 STOP
600  REM  SUBROUTINE TO CALC GAIN & PHASE
610  REM  OF (R1 + J * I1)/(R2 + J * I2) IN DB & RADS
620  REM  RESULT IN G & P .
630  R=R1*R2+I1*I2 : I=I1*R2-I2*R1
640  D=R2*R2+I2*I2 : G=999 : P=0 : P1=3.141592654
650  IF D=0 THEN GOTO 720
660  E=SQR(R*R+I*I)/D : G=-999 : P=-1.5*P1
670  IF E>0 THEN G=20*LOG(E)/LOG(10)
680  IF I<0 THEN P=-P1/2
690  IF R>0 THEN P=ATN(I/R)
700  IF R<0 THEN P=ATN(I/R)-P1
710  IF P>0 THEN P=P-2*P1
720  RETURN

Sample run 1

SAMPLING FREQ (HZ):? 360
NUMERATOR ORDER :? 4
DEMONINATOR ORDER:? 0
ENTER NUMERATOR COEFFS:-
A0:? 0.2
A1:? 0.2
A2:? 0.2
A3:? 0.2
A4:? 0.2
ENTER DENOMINATOR COEFFS:-
B0:? 1
INCREMENT(HZ): 15
```

FREQUENCY	GAIN	PHASE LEAD
(HERTZ)	(DB.)	(DEGREES)
0	0	0
15	-0.604	-30
30	-2.54	-60
45	-6.324	-90

```
 60      -13.979     -120
 75      -27.354     -330
 90      -13.979     -360
105      -12.043      -30
120      -13.979      -60
135      -21.635      -90
150      -25.418     -300
165      -15.915     -330
180      -13.979        0

Sample run 2

SAMPLING FREQ (HZ): ? 2000
NUMERATOR ORDER : 1
DENOMINATOR ORDER :1
ENTER NUMERATOR COEFFS:-
A0:  1
A1 : -1
ENTER DENOMINATOR COEFFS:-
B0 : 1
B2 : -0.42
INCREMENT (HZ) :? 15
FREQUENCY    GAIN    PHASE LEAD
(HERTZ)      (DB.)    (DEGREES)
   0        -999       -270
 100       -5.862    -291.195
 200        1.142    -308.502
 300        0.819    -321.283
 400        1.782    -330.656
 500        2.305    -337.782
 600        2.608    -343.471
 700        2.791    -348.244
 800        2.899    -352.44
 900        2.957    -356.299
1000        2.975       0
```

Program notes

(1) The user specifies a sampling frequency f_s and an 'increment' f_i, both in hertz. The program prints the gain and phase lead at frequency intervals of f_i over the range 0 to $f_s/2$ Hz.

(2) The program converts all frequencies to relative frequencies by multiplying them by $2\pi/f_s$. Entering $f_s = 2\pi$ instead of the true sampling frequency produces a relative frequency scale with all frequencies effectively in radians/sample. Entering $f_s = 360$ produces a relative frequency scale with radians/sample conveniently converted to degrees/sample.

(3) The first sample run analyses the FIR filter in Figure 3.2. Graphs of the gain and phase responses thus produced are shown in Figures 3.7(a) and 3.7(b). A relative frequency scale is used, and the dynamic range of the gain response graph is restricted to 40 dB. The phase response graph produces discontinuities at various points,

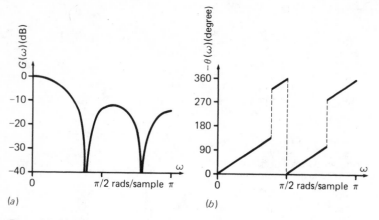

Figure 3.7 (a) Gain response of FIR filter (b) Phase response of FIR filter

with shifts of 180 degrees. The 360 degrees shift at $\omega = \pi/2$ is not a discontinuity and is simply due to the restricted vertical scale of the graph.

(4) The second sample run analyses the IIR filter shown in Figure 3.4, with $f_s = 2000\,\text{Hz}$, to produce the gain and phase response graphs shown in Figures 3.8(a) and 3.8(b).

(5) More points than requested above are generally needed to show all the features of gain and phase responses. If graphs are to be plotted by hand, request more points and select from these, looking for maxima and minima etc.

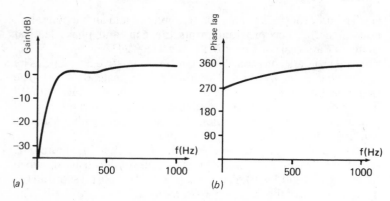

Figure 3.8 (a) Gain response of IIR filter (b) Phase response of IIR filter

3.10 Phase response and group delay

A system whose phase response $\theta(\omega)$ satisfies:

$$-\theta(\omega) = k\omega \qquad (3.38)$$

for constant k is termed linear phase. The effect of such a phase response will be to delay any sinusoidal input sequence by k sampling intervals or $T_s = kT$ seconds referred to as the phase delay, regardless of its frequency. An input signal expressed as a Fourier series of sampled sinusoids will therefore have all these sinusoids delayed by the same amount of time and in the absence of any amplitude changes the output signal will be an exact replica of the input signal delayed by k sampling intervals. This finding may be generalized to any discrete time signal as represented by its DTFT.

It is important to realize that linear systems are not necessarily linear phase and that phase effects can distort a wave shape as well as gain. The group delay function $T_G(\omega)$ for a linear system is defined as:

$$T_G(\omega) = \frac{-\mathrm{d}\theta(\omega)}{\mathrm{d}\omega} \qquad (3.39)$$

and is the slope of the phase lag response graph at any frequency ω. For a linear phase system, $T_G(\omega)$ becomes equal to k which is constant for all ω.

3.11 Poles and zeros

Equation (3.33) expresses the system function of a digital filter as a ratio of two polynominals in z^{-1}. It is sometimes convenient to re-express this equation as:

$$H(z) = z^{(M-N)}\, \frac{a_0 z^N + a_1 z^{N-1} + \ldots + a_N}{b_0 z^M + b_1 z^{M-1} + \ldots + b_M} \qquad (3.40)$$

The numerator and denominator may now be factorized to express $H(z)$ as follows:

$$H(z) = Kz^{(M-N)}\, \frac{(z - z_1)(z - z_2)\ldots(z - z_N)}{(z - p_1)(z - p_2)\ldots(z - p_M)} \qquad (3.41)$$

where $z_1, z_2, \ldots z_N$ are referred to as the zeros of $H(z)$, $P_1, P_2, \ldots P_M$ are the poles of $H(z)$, and K is a constant. Poles and zeros may be real or complex. Since numerator and denominator polynominal coefficients are normally real, poles and zeros which are complex must occur in conjugate pairs. It follows from Equation (3.41) that $H(z) = 0$ when evaluated at a zero and that $H(z)$ is infinite at each pole. Apart from the constant K, $H(z)$ is completely characterized by its poles and zeros. For a causal and stable system, $H(z)$ cannot be infinite for any value of z with $|z| \geq 1$ and it follows that all the poles of $H(z)$ must have modulus less than one. No such restriction applies to the zeros.

Considerable insight into the properties of $H(z)$ may be gained by plotting its poles and zeros on an Argand diagram with horizontal axis as the real part of z and vertical axis as the imaginary part of z. A 'unit circle' is generally drawn to indicate all values of z for which $|z| = 1$. Consider the IIR digital filter shown in Figure 3.4, whose system function is given by Equation (3.28). $H(z)$ for this example has a pole at $z = 0.42$ and a zero at $z = 1$, which are plotted in Figure 3.9 with X marking the pole and 0 marking the zero. The unit circle divides the Argand diagram into three regions: the interior of the circle for which $|z| < 1$, the circle itself and the exterior for which $|z| > 1$. Clearly for a causal and stable system all poles must lie inside the unit circle, and this is the case in Figure 3.9.

The usefulness of this type of diagram may be seen by substituting $z = e^{j\omega}$ into Equation (3.41) to obtain the frequency response of a

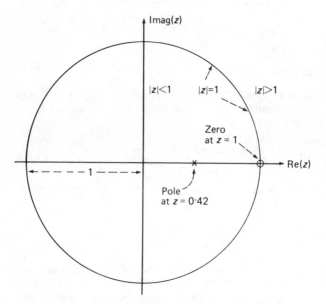

Figure 3.9 Pole and zero plotted on z-plane

general digital filter expressed as:

$$H(e^{j\omega}) = K e^{j(M-N)\omega} \frac{(e^{j\omega} - z_1)(e^{j\omega} - z_2)\dots(e^{j\omega} - z_N)}{(e^{j\omega} - p_1)(e^{j\omega} - p_2)\dots(e^{j\omega} - p_M)} \qquad (3.42)$$

Expressing each denominator and numerator factor in polar form with:

$$(e^{j\omega} - z_i) = |e^{j\omega} - z_i| e^{j\alpha_i(\omega)} \quad \text{for } i = 1, 2, \dots, N \qquad (3.43)$$

and:

$$(e^{j\omega} - p_i) = |e^{j\omega} - p_i| e^{j\beta_i(\omega)} \quad \text{for } i = 1, 2, \dots, M \qquad (3.44)$$

it follows that $H(e^{j\omega}) = G(\omega) e^{j\theta(\omega)}$ with:

$$G(\omega) = \frac{K|e^{j\omega} - z_1| |e^{j\omega} - z_2| \dots |e^{j\omega} - z_N|}{|e^{j\omega} - p_1| |e^{j\omega} - p_2| \dots |e^{j\omega} - p_M|} \qquad (3.45)$$

$$\theta(\omega) = (M - N)\omega + \alpha_1(\omega) + \alpha_2(\omega) + \dots + \alpha_M(\omega)$$

$$- \beta_1(\omega) - \beta_2(\omega) - \dots - \beta_M(\omega) \qquad (3.46)$$

For each zero z_i and a given value of ω, $|e^{j\omega} - z_i|$ is the distance in the Argand diagram from z_i to the point $z = e^{j\omega}$ on the unit circle as indicated in Figure 3.10. The argument, $\alpha_i(\omega)$, of $(e^{j\omega} - z_i)$ is the phase of a vector drawn from z_i to $e^{j\omega}$ as marked in the diagram. A similar diagram may be drawn for each of the poles. It may be

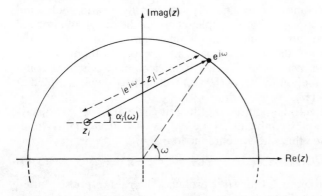

Figure 3.10 Geometric interpretation of modulus and argument of $(e^{j\omega} - z_1)$

deduced that:

$$G(\omega) = K \frac{\text{Product of distances from zeros to } e^{j\omega}}{\text{Product of distances from poles to } e^{j\omega}} \qquad (3.47)$$

$$\theta(\omega) = (M - N)\omega + (\text{sum of phases from zeros to } e^{j\omega})$$
$$- (\text{sum of phases from poles to } e^{j\omega}) \qquad (3.48)$$

The position of a filter's poles and zeros therefore determine the shape of its gain and phase response. The effect of a pole close to the unit circle is to make the denominator of Equation (3.47) small in magnitude for values of ω close to the argument of the pole and this tends to cause a peak in the value of $G(\omega)$. The closer the pole is to the unit circle, the higher the peak can become. Similarly, the effect of a zero close to the unit circle is to make the numerator small thus tending to cause a trough or minimum. Peaks and troughs interact with each other and will cancel each other out if poles and zeros coincide. If a zero happens to be on the unit circle, $G(\omega)$ becomes exactly zero when ω equals the argument of the zero. A pole on the unit circle would make the filter unstable. The effect of the pole and zero illustrated in Figure 3.9 on $G(\omega)$ may be related to the gain response plotted in Figure 3.8(a) to confirm these findings.

Poles and zeros close to the unit circle tend to cause localized changes in group delay (see Equation (3.39) as ω approaches their arguments. The closer a pole or zero is to the unit circle the more dramatic will be the change it produces although, again, effects due to coincident poles and zeros will cancel.

3.12 Design of a notch filter by pole and zero placement

Digital filters may be designed by strategically locating poles and zeros in the z-plane. For example, consider the design of a second order 'notch' filter required to eliminate an unwanted sinusoidal component of the input signal, at $\omega = \pi/3$, without severely affecting the rest of the signal. An application of this filter could be the elimination of 50 Hz (60 Hz) pickup in a signal sampled at 3 kHz (3.6 kHz).

Clearly a zero is required on the unit circle at $z = e^{j\pi/3} = z_1$ say, with its complex conjugate $z_2 = e^{-j\pi/3}$. A second order FIR filter could provide this with system function:

$$H(z) = z^{-2}(1 - z_1)(1 - z_2) = 1 - z^{-1} + z^{-2} \qquad (3.49)$$

Running Program 3.4 for $H(z)$ produces the gain response plotted in Figure 3.11. This graph shows that the objective of eliminating

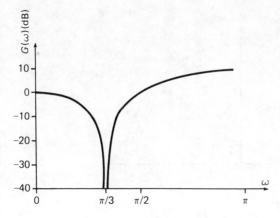

Figure 3.11 Gain response for $H(z) = 1 - z^{-1} + z^{-2}$

the unwanted component at $\omega = \pi/3$ has been achieved at the expense of considerable attenuation of the signal around $\omega = \pi/3$ and an uncalled for emphasis of frequency components close to $\omega = \pi$. The gain response may be improved by placing poles p_1 and p_2 close to z_1 and z_2 respectively as shown in Figure 3.12. Taking $p_1 = 0.9 \, e^{j\pi/3}$ and $p_2 = 0.9 e^{-j\pi/3}$ with z_1 and z_2 as before, the following system function is obtained:

$$H(z) = \frac{(z - z_1)(z - z_2)}{(z - p_1)(z - p_2)} = \frac{1 - z^{-1} + z^{-2}}{1 - 0.9z^{-1} + 0.81z^{-2}} \quad (3.50)$$

which is realized by the signal flow graph shown in Figure 3.13 with $a_0 = a_2 = b_0 = 1$, $a_1 = -1$, $b_1 = -0.9$ and $b_2 = 0.81$. The filter's gain and phase response, again by Program 3.4, is now as shown in Figure 3.14(a) and 3.14(b). It may be observed that although $G(\omega)$ is still zero at $\omega = \pi/3$ the notch is much sharper and significantly affects only a small frequency range. The phase response is clearly non-linear and will produce large variations in group delay around the notch frequency.

The effect on $G(\omega)$ of introducing p_1 and p_2 may now be explained with reference to Equation (3.47). Consider some value of ω not close to $\pi/3$. As indicated by the dotted lines in Figure 3.12, the distances from p_1 and z_1 to $e^{j\omega}$ are approximately equal as are the distances from p_2 and z_2 to $e^{j\omega}$. Hence by Equation (3.47), $G(\omega)$ will be approximately one. Only when ω becomes close to $\pi/3$ will the differences become significant and it may be shown that the 3 dB bandwidth of the notch, i.e. the range of ω for which $G(\omega)$ falls

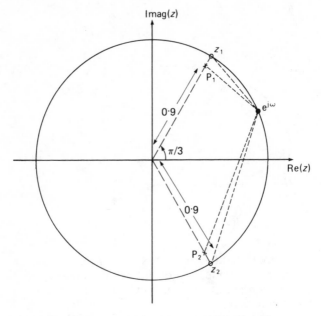

Figure 3.12 Poles and zeros for second-order IIR notch filter

below -3 dB is approximately equal to $2(1 - |p_1|)$ radians/sample which is 0.2 in this case. This range may be reduced still further (at the expense of larger variation in group delay) by moving p_1 and its complex conjugate closer to z_1 and z_2 respectively.

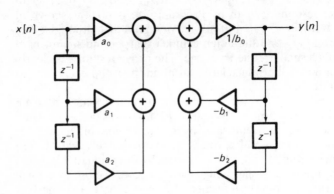

Figure 3.13 'Direct Form 1' signal flow graph

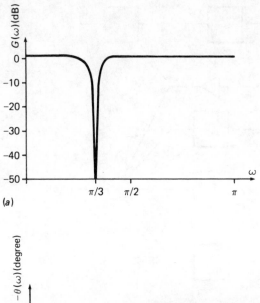

Figure 3.14 (a) Gain response of IIR notch filter (b) Phase response of IIR notch filter

3.13 Realizing IIR digital filters

IIR digital filters of order greater than two are not generally realized by single difference equations since the effects of truncation or rounding error in finite wordlength arithmetic can become very serious as will be explained in Chapter 5. Instead, serial or parallel combinations of second order and possibly first order digital filter sections $L_1, L_2, \ldots, L_N$ are used as illustrated in Figures 3.15(a) and

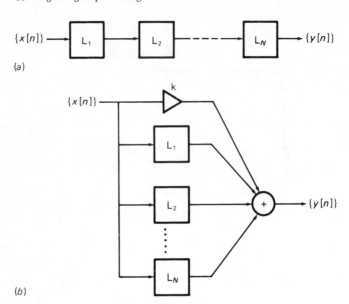

(a)

(b)

Figure 3.15 (a) Serial (cascade) arrangement of biquadratic sections (b) Parallel combination of biquadratic sections

3.15(b). Each section L_i has a system function:

$$H_i(z) = \frac{a_{0i} + a_{1i}z^{-1} + b_{2i}z^{-2}}{b_{0i} + b_{1i}z^{-1} + b_{2i}z^{-2}} \tag{3.51}$$

which represents the difference equation:

$$y_i[n] = \frac{1}{b_{0i}}(a_{0i}x_i[n] + a_{1i}x_i[n-1] + a_{2i}x_i[n-2]$$

$$- b_{1i}y_i[n-1] - b_{2i}y_i[n-2]) \tag{3.52}$$

assuming that $b_{0i} \neq 0$ and that the input and output signals are labelled $x_i[n]$ and $y_i[n]$ respectively. A signal flow graph for this difference equation is shown in Figure 3.13. For first order sections $a_{2i} = b_{2i} = 0$ and the signal flow graph may be simplified. The overall system function is

$$H(z) = H_1(z).H_2(z)\dots H_N(z) \tag{3.53}$$

for a serial combination (cascade) and:

$$H(z) = K + H_1(z) + H_2(z) + \dots + H_N(z) \tag{3.54}$$

for a parallel combination, where *K* is some constant. The overall gain and phase responses for either type of combination may be obtained by running Program 3.5 and entering the coefficients of each second order section.

Program 3.5 ANIIR: gain and phase response of IIR combination

```
10 REM  ANIIR .. ANALYSIS IIR DF IN BIQUAD SECTNS
20 DIM A0(9),A1(9),A2(9),B0(9),B1(9),B2(9)
30 DEF FNR(X)=INT(X*1000+.5)/1000
40 PRINT"SAMPLING FREQ (HZ):"; : INPUT FS
50 PRINT"NUMBER OF SECTNS:"; : INPUT NS
60 PRINT"SERIAL OR PARALLEL (S OR P):"; : INPUT S$
70 K=1
80 IF S$="P"THEN PRINT"ENTER K:";
90 IF S$="P"THEN INPUT K
100 FOR J=1 TO NS
110    PRINT"ENTER COEFFS FOR SECTN ";J;":-"
120    PRINT"A0,A1,A2:"; : INPUT A0(J),A1(J),A2(J)
130    PRINT"B0,B1,B2:"; : INPUT B0(J),B1(J),B2(J)
140 NEXT J : PRINT"OK"
150 PRINT"INCREMENT(HZ)"; : INPUT FI:PRINT
160 PRINT"FREQUENCY","  GAIN","PHASE LEAD"
170 PRINT"(HERTZ)","  DB)","  (DEGREES)"
180 P1=4*ATN(1) : F=0
190 W=2*P1*F/FS: R1=K:I1=0:R2=1:I2=0
200 FOR J=1 TO NS
210    R3=A0(J)+A1(J)*COS(W)+A2(J)*COS(2*W)
220    I3=-A1(J)*SIN(W)-A2(J)*SIN(2*W)
230    R4=B0(J)+B1(J)*COS(W)+B2(J)*COS(2*W)
240    I4=-B1(J)*SIN(W)-B2(J)*SIN(2*W)
250    M=R4*R4+I4*I4 : R=R3 : I=I3
260    IF M=0 THEN R2=0
270    IF M>0 THEN R=(R3*R4+I3*I4)/M
280    IF M>0 THEN I=(I3*R4-R3*I4)/M
290    IF S$="S"THEN 310
300    R1=R1+R : I1=I1+I : GOTO 320
310    R3=R1*R-I1*I : I1=R1*I+I1*R : R1=R3
320 NEXT J
330 GOSUB 600 : REM GET G & P
340 PRINT FNR(F),FNR(G),FNR(P*57.29578)
350 F=F+FI
360 IF F<FS/2+FI THEN GOTO 190
370 END
600 REM  SUBROUTINE TO CALC GAIN,PHASE
610 REM  OF (R1+J*I1)/(R2+J*I2) IN DB & RADS
    Subroutine listing as in Program 3.4

Sample run

SAMPLING FREQ (HZ):? 1
NUMBER OF SECTIONS:? 2
SERIAL OR PARALLEL (S OR P):?P
ENTER K:? 0
ENTER COEFFS FOR SECTN 1:-
A0,A1,A2:? -1.1610,  0.0133, 0
```

```
B0,B1,B2:?  1      ,  -0.4927, 0.3822
ENTER COEFFS FOR SECTN 2:-
A0,A1,A2:? 1.161, 0.08369,   0
B0,B1,B2:?  1      ,  -0.5553, 0.0981
OK
INCREMENT (HZ):? 0.05
```

FREQUENCY	GAIN	PHASE LEAD
(HERTZ)	(DB.)	(DEGREES)
0	0.024	0
0.05	0.022	-37.677
0.1	-0.005	-77.793
0.15	-0.424	-124.948
0.2	-3.062	-179.839
0.25	-8.556	-224.322
0.3	-14.524	-252.943
0.35	-20.019	-273.490
0.4	-25.059	-292.722
0.45	-29.597	-318.546
0.5	-31.956	0

Program notes

(1) First order sections may be accommodated by entering $a_2 = b_2 = 0$.

(2) The sample run is for a fourth order IIR filter composed of two second order sections in parallel. This filter will be encountered in Chapter 5 and has the system function (5.46). The sampling rate is entered as 1 Hz to obtain a normalized frequency scale (a commonly used alternative to relative frequency).

3.14 Alternative structure for second order IIR sections

The signal flow graph shown in Figure 3.13 is often referred to as 'Direct Form I'. There are alternative signal flow graphs available realizing the same second-order transfer function. The most common of these alternatives is obtained by observing that Direct Form I has two subsections which may be rearranged (see Problem 3.8) to obtain the signal flow graph shown in Figure 3.16(a). Figure 3.16(a) may be simplified to Figure 3.16(b), which is Direct Form II, by combining delay elements producing the same signal. This structure is said to be 'canonical' since it minimizes the number of delay operations and therefore minimizes memory requirements.

A Direct Form II signal flow graph for $H_i(z)$ is implemented as a two-stage calculation for each input sample $x_i[n]$:

(i) Calculate $w_i[n] = (b_{0i}x_i[n] - b_{1i}w_i[n-1] - b_{2i}w_i[n-2])/b_{0i}$

$$(3.55)$$

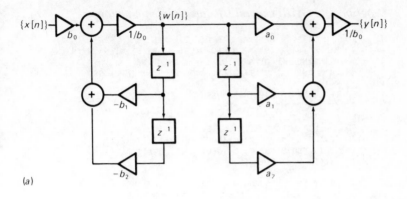

(a)

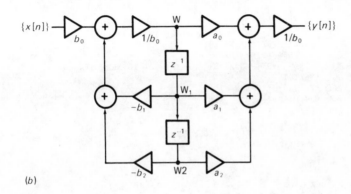

(b)

Figure 3.16 (a) Rearrangement of Direct Form I (b) Direct Form II

(ii) Calculate $y_i[n] = (a_{0i}w_i[n] + a_{1i}w_i[n-1] + a_{2i}w_i[n-2])/b_{0i}$

(3.56)

where $w_i[n]$ is an intermediate sample generated at W in Figure 3.16(b) and $y_i[n]$ is the required output sample. Two previous values of W must have been stored prior to processing $x_i[n]$. These appear at W1 and W2 in Figure 3.16(b) and are initially set to zero. Program 3.6 implements a serial or parallel combination of biquadratic sections each programmed in Direct Form II. The filter arrangement may be tested by a choice of input signals generated by 'subroutine 10000'.

Program 3.6 GIIR: general IIR filter implementation

```
 10 REM GIIR .. GENERAL IIR DIGITAL FILTER
 20 DIM A0(9),A1(9),A2(9),B0(9),B1(9),B2(9),W1(9),W2(9),X(100)
 30 PRINT"NUMBER OF SECTIONS:"; : INPUT NB
 40 PRINT"SERIAL OR PARALLEL(S OR P):"; : INPUT S$
 50 K=1
 60 IF S$="P"THEN PRINT"ENTER K:";
 70 IF S$="P"THEN INPUT K
 80 FOR I=1 TO NB
 90  PRINT"ENTER COEFFS FOR SECTN ";I;":-"
100  PRINT"A0,A1,A2:"; : INPUT A0(I),A1(I),A2(I)
110  PRINT"B0,B1,B2:"; : INPUT B0(I),B1(I),B2(I)
120  W1(I)=0 : W2(I)=0
130 NEXT I : PRINT"OK"
140 PRINT"TEST SEQUENCE LENGTH:"; : INPUT NS
150 GOSUB 10000 : REM GENERATE TEST SEQUENCE
160 PRINT"START OF PROCESSING:"
170 FOR N=0 TO NS-1
180  XI=X(N) : Y=K*XI
190  FOR I=1 TO NB
200   W=(B0(I)*XI-B1(I)*W1(I)-B2(I)*W2(I))/B0(I)
210   YI=(A0(I)*W+A1(I)*W1(I)+A2(I)*W2(I))/B0(I)
220   W2(I)=W1(I) : W1(I)=W
230   IF S$="P"THEN Y=Y+YI
240   IF S$="S"THEN XI=YI : REM INPUT TO NEXT STAGE
250  NEXT I
260  IF S$="S"THEN Y=YI
270  PRINT"X(";N;")=";X(N)," Y(";N;")=";Y
280 NEXT N
290 END
10000 REM ARRAY DEFN SUBROUTINE
      Listing as in Program 1.4
```

Sample run

```
NUMBER OF SECTIONS:? 2
SERIAL OR PARALLEL(S OR P): P
ENTER K:? 0
ENTER COEFFS FOR SECTN 1:-
A0,A1,A2:? -1.161, 0.0133, 0
B0,B1,B2:? 1,    -0.4927, 0.3822
ENTER COEFFS FOR SECTN 2:-
A0,A1,A2:? 1.161, 0.08369, 0
B0,B1,B2:? 1,    -0.5553 , 0.0981
OK
TEST SEQUENCE LENGTH:? 50
SEQUENCE TYPE:? SN
PERIODS OVER 50 SAMPLES? 10
DELAY (IN SAMPLES):? 0
START OF PROCESSING:
X(0)= 0           Y(0) = 0
X(1)= 0.9511      Y(1) = 0
X(2)= 0.5878      Y(2) = 0.1614
X(3)=-0.5878      Y(3) = 0.5363
X(4)=-0.9511      Y(4) = 0.5376
X(5)= 0           Y(5) =-0.6697
```

```
X(6)= 0.9511      Y(6) =-0.6697
X(7)= 0.5878      Y(7) =-0.3723
X(8)=-0.5878      Y(8) = 0.4342
X(9)=-0.9511      Y(9) = 0.6623
X(10)= 0          Y(10)=-0.0122
X(11)= 0.9511     Y(11)=-0.6720
.                 .
.                 .
```

Program note

The sample run produces the response of the IIR filter with system function (5.46), as analysed previously by Program 3.5, to ten cycles of a sinusoidal input of period 5 samples (i.e. of frequency $f_s/5$ Hz or $2\pi/5$ radians/sample). The filter's gain and phase at this frequency (see sample run for Program 3.5) is -3.062 dB and -179.839 degrees respectively. It may be observed that after an initial 'switch-on' transient effect, the filter appears to be settling into a steady state, producing a sinusoidal output approximately 180 degrees out of phase with the input, and with amplitude reduced by a factor 0.707 (-3 dB approximately).

3.15 Reference

1. Oppenheim, A. V. and Schafer, R. W. (1975) *Digital Signal Processing*, Prentice-Hall

Problems

(**3.1**) Write a simple BASIC program to implement the difference Equation (3.2). Determine (a) its impulse response and (b) its response to an input sequence {...0,1,2,3,0,0,0...}. Check your result by running Program 3.3 for the same difference equation and input sequence.

(**3.2**) Draw a signal flow graph for a digital filter with the recursive difference Equation (3.4) and program it in BASIC. Show that its impulse response is identical to that of the FIR filter considered in Section 3.1, thus illustrating that a recursive filter need not be IIR. Why are the sample runs for Programs 3.1 and 3.3 identical?

(**3.3**) Show that difference Equations (2.1) and (2.3) describe LTI digital systems and that (2.5) and (2.6) fail to satisfy the requirements for being LTI.

(**3.4**) Explain the output obtained in the sample run for Program 3.2 by referring to the gain and phase responses shown in Figure 3.8(a) and 3.8(b).

(3.5) Run Program 3.3 to compute the response of the FIR filter shown in Figure 3.2 to the sinusoidal input sequence $\{(\cos{(n\pi/6)})\}$. Explain the output obtained by referring to the gain and phase responses shown in Figures 3.7(a) and 3.7(b).

(3.6) Show that if $\{x[n]\}$ is the input to an LTI system whose system function is $H(z) = z^{-1}$, the output will be $\{x[n-1]\}$. This explains the z^{-1} notation used for delay elements in signal flow graphs.

(3.7) If $\{y[n]\} = \{h[n]\} * \{x[n]\}$ (convolution) show that the DTFT $Y(e^{j\omega})$ of $\{y[n]\}$ is equal to the product of the DTFT of $\{h[n]\}$ and the DTFT of $\{x[n]\}$. This means that discrete time convolution has the same effect as multiplication in the frequency domain.

(3.8) Two LTI systems L_1 and L_2, with impulse responses $\{h_1[n]\}$ and $\{h_2[n]\}$ respectively, are serially cascaded. Calculate the overall impulse response and show that this is not affected by reversing the order of L_1 and L_2.

(3.9) Plot the poles and zeros for the following difference equation on the z-plane and hence estimate the expected form of its frequency response.

$$y[n] = x[n] - 0.9x[n-1] + 0.81x[n-2] + \\ 0.95y[n-1] - 0.9025y[n-2]$$

Confirm your estimation by running Program 3.4 or 3.5, and run Program 3.6 to calculate the impulse response.

(3.10) How could the difference equation given in Problem 3.8 be implemented in Direct Form II if only integer arithmetic were available (Hint: choose a large integer for b_0).

Chapter 4

Digital processing of analogue signals

4.1 Introduction

Digital signal processing systems with analogue/digital interfaces are commonly used to process analogue signals as illustrated in Figure 4.1. Such a scheme may be considered as an alternative to an entirely analogue process and most analogue processes of practical interest can be realized in this way to benefit from the advantages of digital signal processing. It is important to understand the effects of

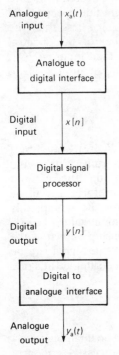

Analogue input $x_a(t)$

Analogue to digital interface

Digital input $x[n]$

Digital signal processor

Digital output $y[n]$

Digital to analogue interface

Analogue output $y_a(t)$

Figure 4.1 Digital processing of an analogue signal

the analogue/digital interfaces and careful consideration must be given to aspects such as sampling and quantisation of the analogue input and reconstruction of an analogue output from the processed digital signal.

4.2 The sampling theorem

It has been shown in Section 2.3.1 (see Equations (2.25) and (2.30)) that if an analogue signal, $x_a(t)$, is sampled at intervals of T seconds to produce a sequence $\{x[n]\}$ where $x[n] = x_a(nT)$ then the DTFT, $X(e^{j\omega})$ of $\{x[n]\}$, is related to the Fourier transform, $X_a(j\Omega)$ of $x_a(t)$ by:

$$X(e^{j\omega}) = \frac{1}{T} \sum_{n=-\infty}^{\infty} X_a(j[\Omega - n\Omega_0]) \tag{4.1}$$

where $\omega = \Omega T$ and $\Omega_0 = 2\pi/T$. The spectrum of the digital signal, $X(e^{j\omega})$, therefore consists of an infinite number of replicas of the analogue signal spectrum, $X_a(j\Omega)$, scaled by the factor $1/T$ and frequency shifted by multiples of Ω_0. This is illustrated in Figure 4.2(b) for an analogue signal having the magnitude spectrum of Figure 4.2(a). Provided the bandwidth of $x_a(t)$ is less than the 'foldover frequency', $\Omega_0/2$, preventing overlap of the spectral replicas as in the case of Figure 4.2(b) rather than Figure 4.2(c), then only components corresponding to $n = 0$ in Equation (4.1) are present in $X(e^{j\omega})$ for $|\Omega| < \Omega_0/2$ and:

$$X(e^{j\omega}) = \frac{1}{T} X_a(j\Omega) \quad |\Omega| < \Omega_0/2 \tag{4.2}$$

The spectrum of the original analogue signal, $X_a(j\Omega)$, scaled by a factor of $1/T$ is therefore retained in the spectrum of its digital counterpart, $X(e^{j\omega})$. It follows that $X_a(j\Omega)$ can be identified without ambiguity given the spectrum, $X(e^{j\omega})$ and therefore, as will be shown, the analogue waveform, $x_a(t)$, can be completely reconstructed from a knowledge only of its sample values $\{x[n]\}$. This is a statement of a very important relationship known as the 'sampling theorem' which asserts that an analogue signal can be reconstructed from its sample values provided it is sampled at a rate greater than twice its bandwidth.

4.2.1 Analogue signal reconstruction

It will now be shown that an analogue signal can be unambiguously reconstructed from a digital signal such as the processed sequence,

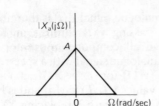

(a)

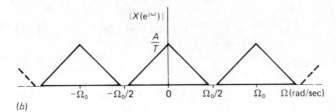

(b)

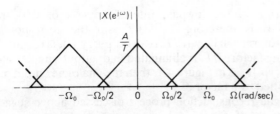

(c)

Figure 4.2 (a) Spectrum of an analogue signal $x_a(t)$ (b) Spectrum of sampled signal $x[n]$ (c) Spectrum of sampled signal $x[n]$ (smaller Ω_0)

$\{y[n]\}$ in Figure 4.1, by an ideal process of digital to analogue conversion and lowpass filtering.

Suppose an ideal digital to analogue converter generates the analogue signal:

$$y_s(t) = \sum_{n=-\infty}^{\infty} y[n]\,\delta(t - nT) \qquad (4.3)$$

where $\delta(t)$ is an analogue impulse (see Section 2.2.3). This signal consists of an infinite sequence of analogue impulses multiplied by successive values of an output sequence, $\{y[n]\}$. The spectrum of $y_s(t)$ is, as discussed in Section 2.3.1 (see Equations (2.23) and (2.25)):

$$Y_s(j\Omega) = \sum_{n=-\infty}^{\infty} y[n]\,e^{-jn\omega T}$$

$$= Y(e^{j\omega}) \qquad (4.4)$$

The spectrum of the analogue signal $y_s(t)$ is therefore identical to that of $\{y[n]\}$, so that passing $y_s(t)$ through an ideal analogue lowpass filter to remove all components greater than $\Omega_0/2$ in frequency, produces an analogue signal with a spectrum identical to that of the digital signal $\{y[n]\}$ for $|\omega| < \pi$. If $y_a(t)$ is the analogue signal which has sample values $y_a(nT) = y[n]$ and is bandlimited to $\Omega_0/2$ then, from Equation (4.1) (with Y replacing X), the spectrum of $\{y[n]\}$ is:

$$Y(e^{j\omega}) = \frac{1}{T} \sum_{n=-\infty}^{\infty} Y_a(j[\Omega - n\Omega_0]) \qquad (4.5)$$

and from Equation (4.2):

$$Y(e^{j\omega}) = \frac{1}{T} Y_a(j\Omega) \quad |\Omega| < \Omega_0/2 \qquad (4.6)$$

The spectrum of the lowpass filtered version of $y_s(t)$ from Equation (4.4) is therefore $Y_a(j\Omega)/T$ and the corresponding analogue waveform will be $y_a(t)/T$. If an output, $y_a(t)$, is required so that the scaling factor, $1/T$, is eliminated and output sample values are given by $\{y[n]\}$, as in Figure 4.1, then the analogue output must also be amplified by a factor of T.

The analogue reconstruction process discussed above suggests the arrangement of Figure 4.3 where the digital to analogue converter approximates $y_s(t)$ by generating narrow, high-amplitude pulses, of width σ and area given by successive values of $\{y[n]\}$. In principle, the approximation could be made arbitrarily close by reducing pulse widths while increasing the amplitudes to maintain

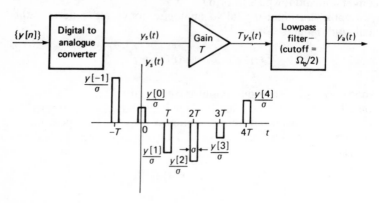

Figure 4.3 Idealized digital to analogue interface

constant pulse areas. In practice it is usual to make the pulse width equal to the sampling period in a technique called 'zero-order hold' which will be discussed further in Section 4.4.2.

4.3 Digital filtering of analogue signals

Equations (4.2) and (4.6) show that, under certain conditions, analogue signals can be passed through the interfaces of Figure 4.1 without distortion. Provided the sampling theorem is satisfied, Equation (4.2) indicates that the spectrum of the analogue input and that of the digital signal formed by taking samples of $x_a(t)$ at intervals of T seconds, are identical up to a frequency of $1/2T$ Hz. (The multiplicative constant $1/T$ in Equation (4.2) is a scaling factor, not a source of distortion). Digital processing of $\{x[n]\}$ results in a digital output $\{y[n]\}$ with spectrum $Y(e^{j\omega})$ and Equation (4.6) shows that a bandlimited analogue output, $y_a(t)$, can be reconstructed with a spectrum identical to $TY(e^{j\omega})$ up to $1/2T$ Hz.

If the processor in Figure 4.1 implements a digital filter with frequency response, $H(e^{j\omega})$, then:

$$Y(e^{j\omega}) = H(e^{j\omega}) X(e^{j\omega}) \qquad (4.7)$$

If $y_a(t)$ is reconstructed by digital to analogue conversion and lowpass filtering as in Figure 4.3 it follows from Equations (4.2) and (4.6) that, in terms of the analogue input and output:

$$Y_a(j\Omega) = \begin{cases} H(e^{j\omega}) X_a(j\Omega), & |\Omega| < \pi/T \\ \\ 0, & |\Omega| > \pi/T \end{cases} \qquad (4.8)$$

where $\omega = \Omega T$. The system of Figure 4.1 therefore appears to have an analogue frequency response of $H(e^{j\Omega T})$ for frequencies up to $1/2T$ Hz and will behave as if an analogue filter of this frequency response had been connected between input and output. This will of course apply only to bandlimited input signals satisfying the sampling theorem. Also, any frequency response realizable by such a scheme is inherently limited to the lowpass filter cutoff of $1/2T$ Hz.

4.4 Sampling and reconstruction in practice

Various practical aspects must be carefully assessed before designing a digital signal processing system based on Figure 4.1.

(a) Real signals are never ideally bandlimited and therefore the sampling rate can never be made strictly greater than twice the highest signal frequency in accordance with the sampling theorem. This introduces a type of distortion called 'aliasing' which will be discussed further in Section 4.4.1.

(b) Ideal impulse function outputs cannot be generated by practical digital to analogue converters. The 'zero-order hold' technique is usually employed and will be discussed in Section 4.4.2.

(c) An ideal lowpass reconstruction filter cannot be implemented because a practical design can only approximate the ideal characteristic. The implications are discussed further in Section 4.4.3.

Strictly, these practical considerations invalidate ideal sampling and reconstruction of analogue signals but although the errors introduced can never be completely eliminated they can usually be reduced to tolerable levels by careful design. The three types of error will now be examined in more detail.

4.4.1 Aliasing error

If the analogue input signal, $x_a(t)$, is not bandlimited to $1/2T$ Hz before sampling at $1/T$ samples per second then frequency components greater than $1/2T$ Hz will overlap as in Figure 4.2(c) and Equation (4.2) will become invalid. Although these components are explicitly shown overlapping in Figure 4.2(c) only their sum is present in the spectrum of the sampled signal and separation of the original analogue spectrum from the unwanted components is normally impossible.

The distorting effect of unwanted components belonging to higher frequency replicas of the analogue input spectrum is called aliasing. As an example, suppose the analogue input is a sinusoid of frequency Ω' and period $T' = 2\pi/\Omega'$ then:

$$x_a(t) = \cos(\Omega' t)$$
$$= \frac{(e^{j\Omega' t} + e^{-j\Omega' t})}{2} \tag{4.9}$$

This signal is the sum of positive and negative components of frequencies $\pm \Omega'$ respectively. The Fourier transform of $\cos(\Omega' t)$ (see Section 2.2.3) is:

$$X_a(j\Omega) = \pi[\delta(\Omega - \Omega') + \delta(\Omega + \Omega')] \tag{4.10}$$

as illustrated in Figure 4.4(a). From Equation (4.1), $X(e^{j\omega})$, the spectrum of the sampled signal, $\{\cos(n\Omega' T)\}$, consists of repetitions of the spectrum of Figure 4.4(a) every Ω_0 radians/second where $\Omega_0 = 2\pi/T$ as shown in Figure 4.4(b). Provided $\Omega' < \Omega_0/2$,

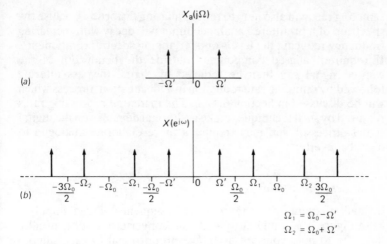

Figure 4.4 (a) Spectrum of sinusoid (b) Spectrum of sampled sinusoid

as in Figure 4.4(b), or equivalently $T < T'/2$, then the two spectral lines corresponding to $\cos(\Omega't)$ in Figure 4.4(a) can be recovered without error from the spectrum of Figure 4.4(b) by ideal lowpass filtering with cutoff $\Omega_0/2$. Since $T < T'/2$, this implies taking more than two samples of $\cos(\Omega't)$ per period. If Ω' is increased then pairs of spectral lines in Figure 4.4(b) will coincide when $\Omega' = \Omega_0/2$ and if $\Omega' > \Omega_0/2$ the lines will cross and only aliased components will be present at frequencies less than $\Omega_0/2$. In this case an inherent ambiguity is introduced since the spectrum of a sampled sinusoid of frequency $(\Omega_0 - \Omega')$ will be identical to that of a sinusoid of frequency Ω' and the recovery filter will output $\cos(\Omega't)$ in both cases. This is also evident in the time domain since:

$$\cos(n[\Omega_0 - \Omega']T) = \cos(2n\pi - n\Omega'T)$$
$$= \cos(n\Omega'T) \qquad (4.11)$$

and exactly the same set of sample values is generated in both cases.

Prefiltering the input by an analogue lowpass filter will reduce the level of frequency components above $1/2T$ Hz resulting in reduced aliased components after sampling. However, a practical filter will always impose a non-ideal lowpass frequency characteristic on the wanted signal below $1/2T$ Hz, particularly in the vicinity of the cut-off frequency. To reduce this effect it is always possible to design a better lowpass prefilter but the improvement for a particular application must be balanced against the extra cost. Increasing the sampling rate will also help to reduce aliasing distortion because the spectrum of a prefiltered analogue input will decay with increasing frequency reducing the levels of overlapping spectral components. If required, aliased components outside the bandwidth of the wanted signal can then be reduced by digital lowpass filtering followed by sampling rate reduction in a 'decimation' process which will be discussed in Section 6.12.2. The increased processing rates required by such techniques make additional demands on the digital signal processor and may require a more elaborate analogue to digital converter.

4.4.2 Zero-order hold

Instead of attempting to approximate a sequence of ideal impulses as in Figure 4.3, a digital to analogue converter output is usually designed to hold constant a voltage proportional to each sample value for the entire duration of each sampling period. This results in the 'staircase' waveform illustrated in Figure 4.5 and is the simplest practical method of interpolating between one sample value and the next. In this case, the 'interpolation function' which determines values of the output signal between samples is the T second pulse, $p(t)$, of unit amplitude illustrated in Figure 4.6. The staircase waveform $y_z(t)$ can be expressed as:

$$y_z(t) = \sum_{n=-\infty}^{\infty} y[n]\, p(t - nT) \qquad (4.12)$$

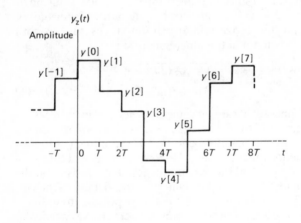

Figure 4.5 Zero-order hold output

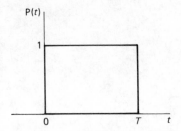

Figure 4.6 Interpolation function for zero-order hold

Taking Fourier transforms to determine the spectrum of $y_z(t)$:

$$Y_z(j\Omega) = \int_{-\infty}^{\infty} \sum_{n=-\infty}^{\infty} y[n]\, p(t-nT)\, e^{-j\Omega t}\, dt$$

$$= \sum_{n=-\infty}^{\infty} y[n] \int_{-\infty}^{\infty} p(t-nT)\, e^{-j\Omega t}\, dt \qquad (4.13)$$

By changing the variable of integration:

$$Y_z(j\Omega) = \sum_{n=-\infty}^{\infty} y[n] \int_{-\infty}^{\infty} p(t)\, e^{-j\Omega(t+nT)}\, dt \qquad (4.14)$$

and since $p(t)$ is non-zero only for $0 \leqslant t \leqslant T$:

$$Y_z(j\Omega) = \sum_{n=-\infty}^{\infty} y[n]\, e^{-jn\Omega T} \int_{0}^{T} 1 \cdot e^{-j\Omega t}\, dt$$

$$= H(j\Omega)\, Y(e^{j\omega}) \qquad (4.15)$$

where $Y(e^{j\omega})$ is the DTFT of $\{y(nT)\}$ and, by modifying the derivation of Equation (2.15) in Section 2.2.2 for a pulse of T seconds:

$$H(j\Omega) = \int_{0}^{T} e^{-j\Omega t}$$

$$= T\, e^{-j\Omega T/2}\, \text{sinc}\,(\Omega T/2) \qquad (4.16)$$

Zero-order hold therefore acts as an interpolating filter with the type of lowpass magnitude response illustrated in Figure 4.7. Because $|H(j\Omega)| \approx T$, for lower frequencies the frequency response will approximate the action of the ideal lowpass filter and amplifier in reconstructing $y_a(t)$ as in Figure 4.3. However, higher frequencies of $Y(e^{j\omega})$ in the region of $\omega = \pi$ will be selectively

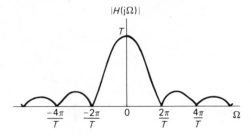

Figure 4.7 Magnitude response of zero-order hold

attenuated in comparison by a factor approaching:

$$\frac{\sin{(\pi/2)}}{(\pi/2)} = 0.637 \approx 4\,\mathrm{dB} \qquad (4.17)$$

In many applications such as voice transmission where higher frequency components are less significant than the lower, this 'droop' in frequency response may not be important but if required, the response can be compensated or 'equalized' by further filtering which aims to impress the reciprocal frequency response $1/H(\mathrm{j}\Omega)$ for $|\Omega| < \pi/T$. This could be achieved by analogue filtering or performed digitally with other digital filtering operations before digital to analogue conversion and reconstruction.

4.4.3 Practical reconstruction filter

The frequency response of a practical filter will deviate from the ideal and will have a finite transition band between the passband and the stopband regions of its frequency response. If the sampling rate is increased a little beyond twice the highest frequency then a 'guard band' will be created in the region of $1/2T$ Hz between the wanted signal spectrum and its first aliased components. This eases the design of the reconstruction filter since the finite transition region between passband and stopband of a practical lowpass filter can be placed in the guard band. In general, the user must select an analogue reconstruction filter to provide acceptable attenuation of aliased components above $1/2T$ Hz without introducing excessive magnitude and phase variations below this frequency. Butterworth and particularly Chebychev filters of various orders are common in this application (see Section 5.9).

4.5 Quantisation of the analogue input

It has been assumed that the analogue to digital interface in Figure 4.1 generates exact sample values from the input analogue signal. However, a practical converter must deliver quantised sample values as the digital signal will have only a finite number of binary digits available to represent each sample value. Errors will therefore be present due to differences between true values and the nearest available quantisation levels. For uniform quantisation, the amplitude scale is divided into equal intervals between maximum and minimum values, $\pm X_{max}$, as illustrated in Figure 4.8 for a 4-bit analogue to digital converter. In this case, 16 levels are available and are uniformly distributed between -8Δ to 7Δ where Δ is the quantisation interval. A 4-bit two's complement code (see Section 1.12.1) is used to represent positive and negative levels and the common practice of placing a quantisation level at zero is followed. (Positive and negative quantisation ranges must therefore be unequal since the total number of available quantisation levels is even. For a large number of quantisation levels this discrepancy is small and in general, it is convenient to take X_{max}, the largest signal magnitude which can be encoded, as the maximum of all level magnitudes: in this case, 8Δ.)

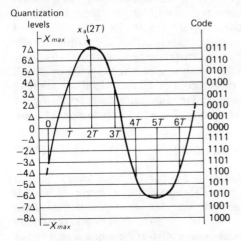

Figure 4.8 Uniform quantization using a 4-bit code

If $x_q(nT)$ denotes the values of quantised samples then, with the nth sample $x_a(nT)$ represented by the nearest available quantisation level, it can be seen from Figure 4.8 that quantisation error is the

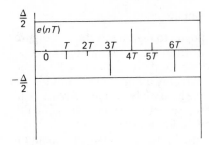

Figure 4.9 Quantization error sequence

difference:

$$e(nT) = x_q(nT) - x_a(nT) \tag{4.18}$$

It follows that provided $|x_a(t)| < X_{max}$, the error magnitude, $|e(nT)| \leq \Delta/2$. The error sequence for 16 level quantisation of the input signal of Figure 4.8 is illustrated in Figure 4.9. If the number of quantisation levels between $\pm X_{max}$ is sufficiently large in relation to the fluctuations of $x(t)$, error values tend to be uniformly distributed over the range $\pm \Delta/2$ as there is no reason why they should concentrate in any particular region within this range. If this is a reasonable assumption then certain results from the theory of random signals can be applied. Since errors are symmetrically distributed about zero the mean error must be zero and it can also be shown (Reference 1) that the mean square error is given by $\Delta^2/12$. Quantisation error can therefore be characterized as additive random noise of known mean and mean square value removing the need to consider the exact values of $e(nT)$ in many applications. Thus:

$$\{x_q(nT)\} = \{x_a(nT)\} + \{e(nT)\} \tag{4.19}$$

and the quantised sequence $\{x_q(nT)\}$ can be regarded as the sum of the 'true' sequence, $\{x_a(nT)\}$ and additive noise of known statistics. If $|x_a(t)|$ does exceed X_{max} for significant periods then this statistical argument will fail as gross 'overload' distortion occurs introducing signal-dependent distortion when signal peaks are 'clipped'. In general, both signal and quantisation noise components will be processed by any subsequent digital signal processing and the statistical approach which has been outlined above allows each to be considered separately in a linear system. For example, in designing a linear digital filter the effect of the filter on the unquantised signal and on the noise can be considered quite independently (Reference 2).

The assumptions which underlie the statistical approach to quantisation error can be tested by Program 4.1 which computes error sequences and their mean and mean square values for various input signals. The number of quantisation levels is taken as 2^B where B is the number of binary digits available for representing each sample on a uniform scale. It follows that if $\Delta = 1$, then $X_{max} = 2^{B-1}$. The theoretical values of mean and mean square error are therefore 0 and 1/12 respectively and Program 4.1 compares these with the exact values calculated for a given input by computing the sequence $\{e[n]\}$ and averaging $e[n]$ and $e^2[n]$ over a given number of samples. Good agreement should be obtained for values of B greater than about 2 provided input signal peaks are in the vicinity of X_{max}. If peak signal values are made less than X_{max} then the extreme quantisation levels will be unused effectively reducing the number of available levels and hence the effective value of B. Also, signal fluctuations must be sufficiently rapid to ensure that an approximately uniform error distribution is obtained over the chosen sequence of input samples.

Program 4.1 QUANTISE: mean and mean square values of quantisation error.

```
10 REM QUANTISE
20 DIM X(200)
30 PRINT "NO. OF SAMPLES, NO. OF BITS";
40 INPUT NS,NB
50 XN=-2^(NB-1) : XM=-XN-1
60 PRINT "QUANTISATION RANGES FROM ";XN;"TO";XM
70 GOSUB 10000 : REM ARRAY DEFN. SUB.
80 M=0 : MS=0
90 PRINT "MULTIPLY INPUT BY";
100 INPUT SC
110 PRINT "INPUT","Q INPUT", "ERROR"
120 FOR N=0 TO NS-1
130 X(N)=SC*X(N)
140 XQ=INT(X(N)+0.5)
150 IF XQ>XM THEN XQ=XM
160 IF XQ<XN THEN XQ=XN
170 ER=XQ-X(N)
180 PRINT X(N),XQ,ER
190 M=M+ER : MS=MS+ER*ER
200 NEXT N
210 PRINT "MEAN=";M/NS
220 PRINT "(PREDICTION = 0)"
230 PRINT "MEAN SQ.=";MS/NS
240 PRINT "(PREDICTION= .0833)"
250 END
```

```
10000 REM - - ARRAY DEFINITION SUB. - -
[- - etc. see Program 1.4 - -]

Sample run

NO. OF SAMPLES, NO. OF BITS ? 10 , 7
QUANTISATION RANGES FROM -64 TO 63
SELECT INPUT SEQUENCE ? SN
SINE WAVE - PERIODS
OVER 10 SAMPLES ? 1.3
NO. SAMPLES DELAY ? 1.5
MULTIPLY INPUT BY ? 64
    INPUT     Q INPUT     ERROR
  -60.2164      -60       .2164
  -25.4175      -25       .4175
   25.4175       25      -.4175
   60.2164       60      -.2164
   57.0244       57      -.0244
   17.8554       18       .1446
  -32.5787      -33      -.4213
  -62.4587      -62       .4587
  -52.9332      -53      -.0668
  -10.0118      -10       .0118
MEAN = .0102
(PREDICTION = 0)
MEAN SQUARE = .0856
(PREDICTION = .0833)
```

Program notes

(1) The array definition subroutine 10000 is used to define the input sequence. Since most signals generated by this subroutine will have unity maximum values the program requests a scaling factor which can be used to adjust the input level relative to X_{max}. If inputs larger in magnitude than X_{max} are used then signal peaks are clipped in statements 150 and 160. If periodic inputs such as the 'SN' option of subroutine 10000 are selected then repeating error patterns due to whole numbers of periods in the input sequence should be avoided as this effectively reduces the number of samples used in obtaining averages.

(2) A 10 sample sinusoidal input sequence with 7-bit quantisation is used for the sample run. To obtain a better agreement with predicted values a larger number of input samples and/or number of bits should be used.

Although Program 4.1 models the quantisation process on the assumption that $x(nT)$ is represented on a continuous scale, the internal representation of numbers by the computer running the program will also introduce quantisation error in its own right. However, this is likely to be negligible compared with the maximum quantisation error which will normally be 0.5.

4.5.1 Signal to quantisation noise ratio

Signal to quantisation noise ratio (SQNR) is the ratio of the mean square value of input signal to the mean square value of quantisation noise and is a useful objective measure of the fidelity of the quantised signal. That is:

$$\text{SQNR} = \frac{\text{mean square value of input signal}}{\text{mean square value of quantisation noise}} \qquad (4.20)$$

Let the mean square value of the signal be S. With uniform quantisation intervals of Δ the mean square quantisation noise is $\Delta^2/12$ and therefore:

$$\text{SQNR} = \frac{12S}{\Delta^2} \qquad (4.21)$$

If B bits are available and the quantisation range is $\pm X_{max}$ then the quantisation interval:

$$\Delta = \frac{2X_{max}}{2^B} \qquad (4.22)$$

Substituting for Δ in Equation (4.21):

$$\text{SQNR} = \frac{3S\,2^{2B}}{X_{max}^2} \qquad (4.23)$$

or, on a dB scale with $\text{SQNR (d}B) = 10\log_{10}(\text{SQNR})$:

$$\text{SQNR (d}B) \approx 6B + 4.8 - 20\log_{10}\left(\frac{X_{max}}{\sqrt{S}}\right) \qquad (4.24)$$

If the signal level is adjusted to fully occupy the quantiser range and if $(X_{max}/\sqrt{S})$, the ratio of the peak to root mean square (rms) value of the input signal, is known then further simplification may be possible. For example, the rms value of a sinusoidal input signal, $A\sin(\omega't)$, is $A/\sqrt{2}$ and therefore the peak to rms value is $\sqrt{2}$. If the signal level is adjusted so that $A = X_{max}$ then, from Equation (4.24), the maximum SQNR becomes:

$$\text{SQNR (dB)} \approx 6B + 1.8 \qquad (4.25)$$

For a signal such as speech $X_{max}/\sqrt{S} = 4$ is a common assumption in which case the maximum SQNR is given by:

$$\text{SQNR (dB)} \approx 6B - 7.3 \qquad (4.26)$$

In this case the signal to noise ratio is degraded by the need to provide uniform quantisation levels for the relatively larger peaks.

Table 4.1

Number of bits	SQNR (dB)
4	17
6	29
8	41
10	53
12	65
14	77
16	89

Maximum SQNR (dB) is listed in Table 4.1 against number of bits on the assumption that $X_{max} = 4\sqrt{S}$ as for Equation (4.26). (This provides an objective guide to the number of bits required for a given fidelity requirement although for a signal such as speech, fidelity is ultimately a subjective matter (Reference 3) which can only be determined by listening tests.)

Equation (4.24) implies that for every extra bit used to represent $x(nT)$ a further 6 dB is added to SQNR (dB). However, a practical upper limit to the number of extra bits which can be used to increase SQNR (dB) will usually be reached when Δ becomes comparable with the inevitable noise level present in the original analogue input. At this point, the use of extra bits only results in a finer representation of analogue noise as the signal to noise ratio of the quantised signal approaches that of the original analogue signal.

4.5.2 Nonuniform quantisation

The estimate of quantisation noise which has been derived above for uniform quantisation is independent of signal amplitude and therefore SQNR will reduce as the input signal is attenuated. In applications such as speech coding where it can be difficult to maintain signal fluctuations within the range of the analogue to digital converter it is common to use a nonuniform quantisation scale to reduce the dependence of SQNR on the level of the analogue input. This can be done by reducing quantisation intervals at low amplitudes at the expense of increasing intervals for the higher amplitudes (Reference 1).

Nonuniform quantisation can also be applied to the efficient coding of analogue signals which have high peak to rms ratios. Because such signals assume higher amplitudes relatively infrequently it becomes advantageous to increase quantisation intervals for the higher amplitudes. If quantisation intervals are made smaller in comparison with uniform quantisation over the more likely lower amplitude ranges then, on average, lower quantisation noise can be obtained for the same number of bits per sample. Alternatively, a smaller number of bits/sample can be employed for the same average level of quantisation noise. Calculation of quantisation noise for nonuniform quantisation involves the probability distribution of the input signal amplitude and is considerably less straightforward than for the uniform case (Reference 1).

It should be noted that linear operations such as digital filtering cannot be performed directly on a non-uniformly quantised sequence without code conversion since such a sequence represents a distorted version of the original signal. It is usually necessary to convert from nonuniform to uniform quantisation scales before linear processing is performed and, if necessary, back to non-uniform after processing.

4.6 Nonlinear signal processing

Nonlinear signal processing and non-time-invariant processing requires special consideration because frequency components are generated which are not present in the input. For example, consider a nonlinear process where each digital signal sample of an input $\{x[n]\}$ is squared to produce an output sequence $\{x^2[n]\}$. If $\{x[n]\}$ is the sampled sinusoid $\{\cos(\omega'n)\}$, squaring generates the output:

$$\{\cos^2(\omega'n)\} = 0.5\{1 + \cos(2\omega'n)\} \tag{4.27}$$

consisting of a sampled sinusoid of twice the original frequency plus a constant. Provided $\omega' < \pi/2$, the correct analogue output will be obtained after digital to analogue conversion and lowpass filtering with cutoff frequency $1/2T$ Hz. However, if $\omega' > \pi/2$ the output cannot be correctly represented as the frequency of the sinusoidal analogue component will exceed the $1/2T$ Hz limit. Because a component of frequency ω' cannot be distinguished from one of frequency $(2\pi - \omega')$, as discussed in Section 4.4.1, an aliased component will appear with a lower frequency than expected. For example, if $\omega' = \pi/4$ then the digital output becomes $0.5[1 + \cos(n\pi/2)]$ and the component at $\pi/2$ can be correctly recovered at the output but if $\omega' = 3\pi/4$ the digital output becomes:

$$0.5[1 + \cos(3\pi n/2)] = 0.5[1 + \cos(n\pi/2)] \tag{4.28}$$

resulting in an identical but erroneous output.

This illustrates that aliasing can occur not only due to 'undersampling' an analogue signal as discussed in Section 4.4.1 but also as the result of nonlinear processing which, if performed directly on the analogue signal, would increase its bandwidth to beyond $1/2T$ Hz. The remedy is to ensure that the sampling rate is high enough to properly represent the expected bandwidth of the output. In the case of the above squaring process the sampling rate should be made more than 4 times the frequency of the input sinusoid. The resulting 'oversampling' by the analogue to digital converter may seem wasteful but such a sequence can be obtained digitally by an interpolation procedure (see Section 6.12.1) so that only the processor and digital to analogue converter need operate at the higher sampling rate. In general, it may be difficult to determine the extent of significant high frequency components generated by a nonlinear process but if this is the case an experimental approach can be followed by gradually increasing the sampling rate until the reconstructed signal is acceptably free of aliased components for suitable test signals.

4.7 References

1. Jayant, N. S. and Noll, P. (1984) *Digital Coding of Waveforms*, Prentice-Hall
2. Roberts, R. A. and Mullis, C. T. (1987) *Digital Signal Processing*, Addison-Wesley
3. Rabiner, L. R. and Schafer, R. W. (1978) *Digital Processing of Speech Signals*, Prentice-Hall

Problems

(4.1) The analogue signals $\cos(2\pi f't)$ and $\sin(2\pi f't)$ are sampled at a rate of 8000 samples per second. Sketch time and frequency domain representations for both signals when $f' = 1$ kHz (see Section 4.4.1). Repeat with the frequency of both signals increased to exactly 4 kHz. Which signals, if any, can now be reconstructed without ambiguity? In general, what can be deduced about sampling and reconstruction of the signal $\cos(2\pi f't + \theta)$ where f' is exactly half the sampling frequency and θ is a constant phase angle? (Hint: apply $\cos(A + B)$ formula).

(4.2) A signal reconstruction scheme generates an analogue waveform from a sequence of samples by connecting each sample value to the next by a straight line segment (rather than holding constant for T seconds). Identify the interpolation function and hence determine the nature of spectral distortion introduced by this scheme. Is there an improvement over zero-order hold (see Section 4.4.2)?

(4.3) Determine the effect on the reconstructed analogue signal and its spectrum of making the hold time in the zero-order hold scheme half (rather than equal to) the sampling period T. Could distortion be reduced to arbitrarily low levels by making the hold time even smaller?

(**4.4**) Construct special waveforms for which quantisation error is always (a) zero (b) $\Delta/2$. Use Program 4.1 to confirm that the mean square quantisation error is then 0 and $\Delta^2/4$ respectively. Why does $\Delta^2/12$ not provide a good estimate of mean square error for these waveforms?

(**4.5**) A certain analogue signal has a peak/rms ratio of $6:1$ and a bandwidth of 5 kHz. How many bits per sample would be required to maintain a signal to quantisation noise ratio better than 40 dB using uniform quantisation?

(**4.6**) Modify Program 4.1 to evaluate SQNR (dB) by direct measurement on the input signal and compare the results with the predictions of Equations (4.25) and (4.26).

(**4.7**) A digital signal processing system is required to generate the analogue output $\sqrt{(1 + x_a(t))}$ where $x_a(t)$ is a real input signal of bandwidth 1 kHz. If $|x_a(t)| < 1$ what sampling rate should be used if (a) $|x_a(t)|^3$ can be considered negligible? (b) $|x_a(t)|^2$ can be considered negligible? (Hint: use the binomial theorem to express the square root as a power series.)

Chapter 5

Digital filter design

5.1 Introduction

The design of digital filters involves two distinct operations: approximation and realization. Approximation is used to derive a realizable system function from some idealized 'target' specification. Realization concerns the formulation of a signal flow graph and its implementation in hardware or software. Neither of these operations necessarily has a unique outcome as a given target specification can usually be approximated by many system functions and a given system function can have many possible realizations. The differences between alternative realizations become particularly important when fixed point arithmetic is used and the effect of quantisation become significant. Target specifications are often described in terms of idealized frequency responses. For example, bandpass, lowpass, highpass and bandstop frequency responses are commonly required with properties similar to corresponding analogue frequency responses [References 1,2]. This chapter is concerned with the design of FIR and IIR digital filters to meet specifications described in the frequency domain.

5.2 FIR digital filter design by Fourier series approximation

The object of most FIR digital filter design methods is to produce a causal and finite impulse response which can be realized by a transversal filter as illustrated in Figure 5.1. Given some ideal or

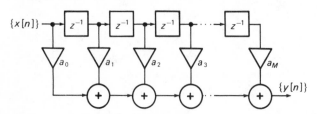

Figure 5.1 FIR digital filter of order M

target frequency response $H(e^{j\omega}) = G(\omega)\, e^{j\theta(\omega)}$ the inverse DTFT formula (2.35) produces a sequence:

$$h[n] = \frac{1}{2\pi} \int_{-\pi}^{\pi} H(e^{j\omega})\, e^{j\omega n}\, d\omega \quad \text{for } n = 0, \pm 1, \pm 1, \dots \qquad (5.1)$$

such that:

$$H(e^{j\omega}) = \sum_{n=-\infty}^{\infty} h[n]\, e^{-j\omega n} \qquad (5.2)$$

A digital filter with impulse response $\{h[n]\}$ as defined by Equation (5.1) would have exactly the target frequency response since $H(e^{j\omega})$ is the DTFT of $\{h[n]\}$. However, this sequence can have non-zero values extending from $n = -\infty$ to $n = +\infty$ and is therefore not necessarily a finite and casual impulse response. The Fourier series approximation method produces a realizable sequence in two stages:

(1) $\{h[n]\}$ is truncated to a finite impulse response by setting $h[n]$ to zero for all values of n outside the range $-M/2 \leqslant n \leqslant M/2$ where M is in the order of the required FIR filter (assumed even).
(2) The sequence is delayed by $M/2$ samples to ensure that the first non-zero sample occurs at $n = 0$.

The resulting sequence is implemented as the impulse response of the FIR filter shown in Figure 5.1 by setting $a_n = h[n]$ for $n = 0, 1, 2, \dots, M$.

5.2.1 Design of bandpass lowpass and highpass FIR filters

Consider the design of a bandpass digital filter with:

$$G(\omega) = \begin{cases} 1 & \omega_1 \leqslant |\omega| \leqslant \omega_2 \\ 0 & |\omega| < \omega_1 \text{ and } \omega_2 < |\omega| \leqslant \pi \end{cases} \qquad (5.3)$$

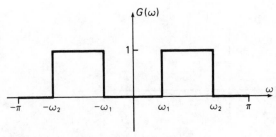

Figure 5.2 Ideal bandpass gain response

as illustrated in Figure 5.2. The filter is required to pass unattenuated all frequency components in the relative frequency range ω_1 to ω_2, and eliminate all components in the ranges 0 to ω_1 and ω_1 to π. Frequency ω_1 may be set to zero, in which case the filter may be termed 'lowpass'. If $\omega_1 > 0$ and $\omega_2 = \pi$, the filter is termed 'highpass'. Taking $\theta(\omega) = 0$ for all ω:

$$h[n] = \frac{1}{2\pi} \int_{\omega_1}^{\omega_2} e^{j\omega n}\, d\omega + \frac{1}{2\pi} \int_{-\omega_2}^{-\omega_1} e^{j\omega n}\, d\omega$$

$$= \begin{cases} \dfrac{1}{\pi n}\left(\sin\left(\omega_2 n\right) - \sin\left(\omega_1 n\right)\right) & n \neq 0 \\[2ex] \dfrac{1}{\pi}\left(\omega_2 - \omega_1\right) & n = 0 \end{cases} \tag{5.4}$$

The sequence $\{h[n]\}$ is illustrated in Figure 5.3 in the case where $\omega_1 = 0$ and $\omega_2 = \pi/2$. Truncating the sequence for $M = 10$ and delaying by $M/2 = 5$ samples, gives the following FIR sequence:

$$\{\ldots, 0, 1/5\pi, 0, -1/3\pi, 0, 1/\pi, 1/2, 1/\pi, 0, -1/3\pi, 0, 1/5\pi, 0, \ldots\} \tag{5.5}$$

which may be realized by a tenth-order transversal filter as illustrated in Figure 5.1 with:

$$a_0 = 1/5\pi, a_1 = 0, a_2 = -1/3\pi, \ldots, a_{10} = 1/5\pi$$

The gain and phase response of the FIR filter may be obtained by running Program 3.4. Graphs of these responses are shown in Figure 5.4. Clearly, the graphs differ from the ideal specification in

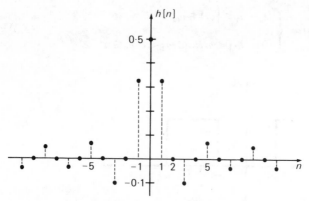

Figure 5.3 Impulse reponse of ideal lowpass filter: cut-off $\pi/2$

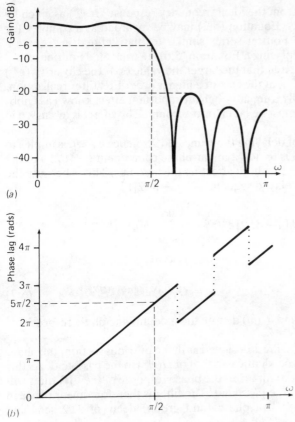

Figure 5.4 (a) Gain response of tenth-order FIR low-pass filter (b) Phase response of tenth-order FIR lowpass filter

that the gain response exhibits a rather gradual transition from passband to stopband with 'ripples' occurring in the stopband. Also, the phase response is not zero for all frequencies, although a linear phase response is observed throughout the passband. The reasons for these discrepancies will now be examined.

5.3 Analysis of Fourier series approximation method

Consider first the effect of truncating $\{h[n]\}$ at stage 1 of the design process. The truncated sequence produces a frequency response:

$$H_T(e^{j\omega}) = \sum_{n=-M/2}^{M/2} h[n]\,e^{-j\omega n} \qquad (5.6)$$

which differs from the ideal frequency response $H(e^{j\omega})$ as given by Equation (5.2). Equation (5.2) may be regarded as a complex (or 'exponential') Fourier series similar to that defined in Equation (2.5) with ω replacing t. Equation (5.6) is a truncated Fourier series. It may be expected that the larger the value of M the closer $H_T(e^{j\omega})$ will be to $H(e^{j\omega})$, at the cost of a higher order FIR filter realization. This is generally true, although an important effect known as Gibbs phenomenon must be taken into account. This effect is discussed in Section 5.5.

The effect of delaying the truncated sequence by $M/2$ samples to make it causal is to add a linear phase component $(-M/2)\omega$ to the phase of $H_T(e^{j\omega})$ without affecting the modulus. This is because the DTFT of the delayed sequence $\{h[n-M/2]\}$ is

$$\sum_{n=0}^{M} h[n-M/2]\, e^{-j\omega n} = \sum_{n=-M/2}^{M/2} h[n]\, e^{-j\omega(n+M/2)}$$

$$= e^{-j(M/2)\omega}\, H_T(e^{j\omega})$$

$$= G_T(\omega)\, e^{j(\theta_T(\omega)-(M/2)\omega)} \tag{5.7}$$

where $G_T(\omega)$ and $\theta_T(\omega)$ denote the modulus and phase respectively of $H_T(e^{j\omega})$.

For bandpass filters designed as in the previous section, the phase of $H_T(e^{j\omega})$ will be identical to that of $H(e^{j\omega})$ in the passband. As this was taken as zero for all ω, the phase response of the FIR filter will be $-(M/2)\omega$ in the passband. The filter is therefore linear phase in the passband with a phase (and group) delay of $M/2$ sampling intervals.

5.4 Quadrature phase FIR filters

It is sometimes useful to design an FIR bandpass filter whose phase response has a 90 degrees offset as compared with a linear phase filter of the same order. Such a 'quadrature phase' FIR filter may be designed by the Fourier series approximation method by taking the phase $\theta(\omega)$ of $H(e^{j\omega})$ to be:

$$\theta(\omega) = \begin{cases} -\pi/2 & : \ \omega > 0 \\ 0 & : \ \omega = 0 \\ \pi/2 & : \ \omega < 0 \end{cases} \tag{5.8}$$

in the first instance instead of zero for all ω. Taking the bandpass gain specification (5.3), the ideal impulse response becomes:

$$h[n] = \frac{1}{2\pi} \int_{\omega_1}^{\omega_2} e^{-j\pi/2} e^{j\omega n} \, d\omega + \frac{1}{2\pi} \int_{-\omega_2}^{-\omega_1} e^{j\pi/2} e^{j\omega n} \, d\omega$$

$$= \begin{cases} \dfrac{1}{\pi n} \left(\cos(\omega_1 n) - \cos(\omega_2 n) \right) & : \quad n \neq 0 \\ \\ 0 & : \quad n = 0 \end{cases} \tag{5.9}$$

When $\omega_1 = 0$, $\omega_2 = \pi/2$ and $M = 10$, this formula produces the following finite impulse response after truncating to $-M/2 \leqslant n \leqslant M/2$ and delaying by $M/2$ samples:

$$\{\ldots, 0, -1/5\pi, 0, -1/3\pi, -1/\pi, -1/\pi, 0, 1/\pi, 1/\pi, 1/3\pi, 0, 1/5\pi, 0, \ldots\} \tag{5.10}$$

It may be observed that whereas the impulse response of a linear phase FIR filter is symmetric about $n = M/2$, the impulse response of a quadrature phase FIR filter has odd symmetry about $n = M/2$.

5.5 Using windows to improve the gain response

If the lowpass design of Section 5.2.1 is repeated with $M = 20$ rather than $M = 10$, the gain response of Figure 5.5 is obtained. The phase response remains linear in the passband with a slope (phase delay) of ten. Although the gain response has been improved by an increase in the cut-off rate and an increase in the number

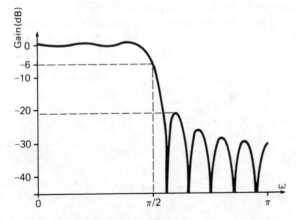

Figure 5.5 FIR lowpass gain response (order 20): rectangular window

of stopband ripples which decrease in amplitude as ω increases, the amplitude of the maximum stopband ripple remains at about $-21\,\text{dB}$. Even if M were further increased, the level of the maximum stop band ripple would not be significantly reduced. This is a wellknown property of Fourier series approximations, known as Gibbs phenomenon (Reference 3).

Gibbs phenomenon arises from the truncation of $\{h[n]\}$ at stage 1 of the design process which effectively multiplies each sample $h[n]$ by:

$$r[n] = \begin{cases} 1 & : -M/2 \leqslant n \leqslant M/2 \\ 0 & : |n| > M/2 \end{cases} \qquad (5.11)$$

to produce the FIR sequence $\{h[n]r[n]\}$. This multiplication process is often called 'windowing' and the sequence $\{r[n]\}$ is a 'rectangular window'. The effect of Gibbs phenomenon may be reduced by replacing $\{r[n]\}$ by a 'Hann window' $\{w[n]\}$ whose elements are:

$$w[n] = \begin{cases} 0.5 + 0.5\cos(\pi n/(1 + M/2)) & : -M/2 \leqslant n \leqslant M/2 \\ 0 & : |n| > M/2 \end{cases} \qquad (5.12)$$

This sequence is illustrated in Figure 5.6 for $M = 16$. Multiplying each sample of $\{h[n]\}$ by $w[n]$ truncates $\{[h[n]\}$ to an FIR sequence as with the rectangular window. However, samples are also progressively reduced in magnitude as n approaches $M/2$ or $-M/2$ from the centre at $n = 0$.

The effect of using a Hann window rather than a rectangular window may be illustrated by reconsidering the example given in Section 5.2.2. This may be done by running Program 5.1 which implements the Fourier series approximation method with a choice of windows including Hann. Specifying a tenth-order linear phase bandpass filter with lower and upper cut-off frequencies at zero and

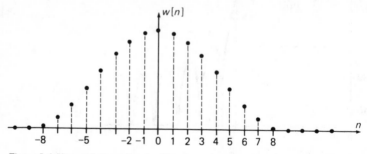

Figure 5.6 Hann window of order 16

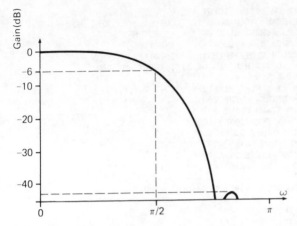

Figure 5.7 FIR lowpass gain response (order 10): Hann window

one quarter of the sampling frequency respectively (corresponding to 0 and $\pi/2$ radians/sample) produces an FIR filter whose frequency response is illustrated in Figure 5.7. It may be observed that the stopband ripples have been greatly reduced at the expense of a less rapid transition between passband and stopband. The cut-off rate may be improved without decreasing stopband attenuation by increasing the filter order.

A large number of different window types, offering different compromises between cut-off rate and ripple level, have been extensively studied (References 1–4). Two common alternatives to the Hann window are the Hamming window and the Kaiser window which are incorporated in Program 5.1. The Hamming window is very similar to the Hann window but offers some improvement in ripple rejection for a similar cut-off rate. The Kaiser window offers a trade-off between cut-off rate and ripple rejection, controlled by a selectable parameter α. When $\alpha = 0$, the Kaiser window is identical to a rectangular window, and when $\alpha = 5.44$ a Hamming window is obtained. The designer may experiment with other values. Program 5.1 can design bandstop as well as bandpass FIR filters by means of a minor modification (see Problem 5.2).

Program 5.1 FSA: FIR filter design by Fourier series approximation

```
10  REM PROGRAM FSA
20  DIM A(100)
30  PRINT"FIR DIGITAL FILTER DESIGN"
40  PRINT"SAMPLING RATE (HZ)"; : INPUT FS
```

```
 50   PRINT"BP OR BS"; : INPUT TY$
 60   PRINT"LINEAR OR QUAD PHASE (L OR Q)"; : INPUT LQ$
 70   PRINT"ORDER(MUST BE EVEN)"; : INPUT M
 80   PRINT"LOWER C/O FREQ(HZ)"; : INPUT FL
 90   PRINT"UPPER C/O FREQ(HZ)"; : INPUT FU
100   PRINT"WINDOW(R,HAN,HAM OR K)";:INPUT W$
105   P1=3.141592654
110   N=INT(M/2) : WL=2*P1*FL/FS : WU=2*P1*FU/FS
120   IF LQ$="L"THEN GOSUB 200
130   IF LQ$="Q"THEN GOSUB 300
140   IF W$="HAN"THEN GOSUB 400
150   IF W$="HAM"THEN GOSUB 500
160   IF W$="K"THEN GOSUB 600
170   PRINT'"COEFFICIENTS ARE:-"
180   FOR J=0 TO M : PRINT"A";J;": ";A(J) : NEXT J
190   STOP
200   REM SUBROUTINE FOR IDTFT (LINEAR PHAS)
210   FOR J=0 TO M : I=J-N
220   IF I=0 THEN GOTO 260
230   A(J)=(SIN(I*WU)-SIN(I*WL))/I/P1
240   IF TY$="BS"THEN A(J)=-A(J)
250   GOTO 280
260   A(J)=(WU-WL)/PI
270   IF TY$="BS"THEN A(J)=1-A(J)
280   NEXT J : RETURN
300   REM SUBROUTINE FOR IDTFT (QUAD PHASE):-
310   FOR J=0 TO M : I=J-N : A(J)=0
320   IF I=0 THEN GOTO 350
330   A(J)=(COS(I*WL)-COS(I*WU))/I/P1
340   IF TY$="BS"THEN A(J)=(1-COS(I*PI))/I/P1 -A(I)
350   NEXT J : RETURN
400   REM SUBROUTINE TO APPLY HANN WINDOW
410   FOR J=0 TO M : I=J-M/2
420   W=0.5*(1+COS(PI*I/(M/2+1)))
430   A(J)=A(J)*W
440   NEXT J : RETURN
500   REM SUBROUTINE TO APPLY HAMMING WINDOW
510   FOR J=0 TO M : I=J-M/2
520   W=0.54+0.46*COS(PI*I*2/M)
530   A(J)=A(J)*W
540   NEXT J : RETURN
600   REM SUBROUTINE TO APPLY KAISER WINDOW
610   PRINT"ENTER ALPHA: "; : INPUT AL
620   FOR J=0 TO M : I=J-M/2
630   X=AL*SQR(1-I*I*4/M/M):DE=1:E=1
640   FOR K=1 TO 25
650   DE=DE*X/K/2:E=E+DE*DE
660   NEXT K : DE=1:F=1
670   FOR K=1 TO 25
680   DE=DE*AL/K/2:F=F+DE*DE
690   NEXT K
700   W=E/F : A(J)=A(J)*W
710   NEXT J : RETURN
```

Sample run

FIR DIGITAL FILTER DESIGN

```
SAMPLING RATE(HZ)? 1000
BP OR BS? BP
LINEAR OR QUAD PHASE(L OR Q)? L
ORDER(MUST BE EVEN)? 10
LOWER C/O FREQ(HZ)? 0
UPPER C/O FREQ(HZ)? 250
WINDOW(R,HAN,HAM OR K)? HAN

COEFFICIENTS ARE:-
A0:  0.004265
A1:  0
A2:  -0.05305
A3:  0
A4:  0.29699
A5:  0.5
A6:  0.29699
A7:  0
A8:  -0.05305
A9:  0
A10:  0.004265
```

Program notes

(1) The program designs FIR bandpass (BP) and bandstop (BS) digital filters. Lowpass and highpass filters are considered as bandpass for the purposes of this program. The user enters a sampling rate and two cut-off frequencies in Hertz. The program automatically converts the cut-off frequencies to radians/sample. A linear (L) or quadrature (Q) phase response may be selected and a choice of four windows is offered: rectangular (R), Hann (HAN), Hamming (HAM) and Kaiser (K). Formulae for these windows may be found in References 1–4 and elsewhere.

(2) The sample run designs a tenth order lowpass with cut-off frequency 250 Hz and linear phase in the passband. The sampling rate is 1000 Hz and therefore the relative cut-off frequency is $\pi/2$ radians/sample. A Hann window is selected. The coefficients of the resulting FIR filter are A0, A1, ..., A10 as printed out.

5.6 FIR digital filter design by frequency sampling

The Fourier series method described in Section 5.2 depends on the availability of a Fourier series expansion for the target frequency response $H(e^{j\omega})$. This was easily obtained for a bandpass frequency response but for less regular functions it may be more difficult or even impossible to obtain a closed expression for the integral of Equation (5.1). An alternative approach is provided by the 'frequency sampling' method which derives an approximation to the required Fourier series through the inverse DFT expression (2.47) as defined in Section 2.4.

Consider a finite sequence $\{H[k]\}_{1,2N}$ consisting of $2N + 1$ samples of some target frequency response $H(e^{j\omega})$ specified at intervals of $2\pi/(2N + 1)$ radians per sample over the relative frequency range $0 \leqslant \omega < 2\pi$. The modulus and phase of $H(e^{j\omega})$ may be chosen arbitrarily for $0 \leqslant \omega < \pi$ except that when $\omega = 0$, $H(e^{j\omega})$ must be real. When $\omega \geqslant \pi$, $H(e^{j\omega})$ must be equal to the complex conjugate of $H(e^{j(2\pi - \omega)})$. Therefore:

$$H[k] = H(e^{j2\pi k/(2N+1)}) \text{ for } k = 0, 1, \ldots, N \qquad (5.13)$$

with $H[k]$ equal to the complex conjugate of $H[2N + 1 - k]$ when $N < k \leqslant 2N$. $\{H[k]\}_{0,2N}$ may be regarded as the DFT of a finite sequence of $2N + 1$ samples: $\{[h[n]]\}_{1,2N}$. By the inverse DFT formula (2.47), the samples of this sequence are:

$$h[n] = \frac{1}{(2N + 1)} \sum_{k=0}^{2N} H[k] \, e^{j2\pi nk/(2N+1)} \quad \text{for } n = 0, 1, 2, \ldots, 2N$$

$$(5.14)$$

Since the DFT of $\{h[n]_{0,2N}$ is $\{H[k]\}_{0,2N}$, the frequency response of an FIR filter with impulse response:

$$\{h[n]\} = \{\ldots, 0, \ldots, 0, h[0], h[1], \ldots, h[2N], 0, \ldots, 0, \ldots\}$$

will be equal to the target frequency response $H(e^{j\omega})$ at the $2N + 1$ frequency sampling points defined above. The FIR filter's frequency response may deviate from $H(e^{j\omega})$ between sampling points, and N must be large enough to ensure that the target frequency response is properly characterised. Once $\{h[n]\}$ has been defined for a suitably large value of N, the sequence may be truncated to reduce the order of the FIR filter. The sequence thus obtained should be close to what would have been obtained by the Fourier series approximation method. The application of a non-rectangular window (e.g. Hann or Kaiser) can offer advantages as discussed in Section 5.5.

As an example, consider the design of an Mth order FIR filter with target gain and phase responses:

$$G(\omega) = \begin{cases} |\omega| & : |\omega| \leqslant 2\pi/3 \\ \\ 0 & : 2\pi/3 < |\omega| < \pi \end{cases}$$

$$\theta(\omega) = \begin{cases} -\pi/2 - \omega M/2 & : \omega > 0 \\ 0 & : \omega = 0 \\ \pi/2 + \omega M/2 & : \omega < 0 \end{cases} \qquad (5.15)$$

The response of a filter with these idealized gain and phase responses to an input signal $\{\cos(\omega n)\}$ would be $\{-\omega \sin(\omega(n - M/2))\}$

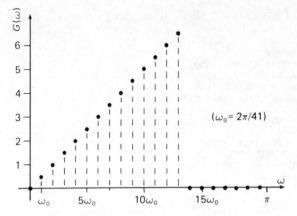

Figure 5.8 Frequency sampled target gain response

when $|\omega| \leqslant 2\pi/3$. Therefore the required filter may be termed a lowpass differentiator with a relative cut-off frequency of $2\pi/3$ and a delay of $M/2$ sampling intervals which must be included for realizability. Figure 5.8 illustrates the target gain response sampled at intervals of $\omega_0 = 2\pi/(2N+1)$ over the range $0 \leqslant \omega < \pi$, with $N = 20$.

Program 5.2 is a general FIR digital filter design program based on the frequency sampling method. This program may be run for the example described above to obtain, using a Kaiser window with $\alpha = 3$, a 14th order FIR filter whose passband phase response is exactly $\theta(\omega)$ as given in Equation (5.15) and whose gain response is illustrated in Figure 5.9.

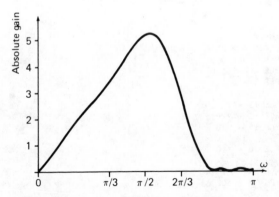

Figure 5.9 FIR lowpass differentiator (order 14)

Program 5.2 FREQSAMP: FIR filter design by frequency sampling

```
10   REM FREQSAMP
20   DIM HM(100),HA(100),A(100)
30   PRINT"VALUE OF N";:INPUT N
40   L=N+N+1 : P=3.141592654
50   PRINT"NEED ";N+1;" FREQ SAMPLES:-"
60   FOR I=0 TO N
70   PRINT"MODULUS OF SAMPLE ";I;" =";
80   INPUT HM(I)
90   NEXT I : PRINT"OK"
100  PRINT"FIR FLTR ORDER(EVEN):";:INPUT M
110  PRINT"LINEAR OR QUAD PHASE(L OR Q)";
120  INPUT LQ$
130  FOR I=1 TO N
140  IF LQ$="L"THEN HA(I)=-I*M*P/L
150  IF LQ$="Q"THEN HA(I)=-P/2-I*M*P/L
160  NEXT I : HA(0)=0
170  FOR I=N+1 TO L-1
180  HM(I)=HM(L-I) : HA(I)=-HA(L-I)
190  NEXT I
200  REM WINDOWED INVERSE DFT (REAL PT ONLY):-
210  FOR I=0 TO M
220  A(I)=0
230  FOR K=0 TO L-1
240  T=2*P*I*K/L
250  A(I)=A(I)+HM(K)*COS(T+HA(K))
260  NEXT K
270  A(I)=A(I)/L
280  NEXT I
290  GOSUB 600 : REM KAISER WINDOW
300  PRINT"COEFFICIENTS ARE:-"
310  FOR I=0 TO M : PRINT "A"; I;": "; A(I):NEXT I
320  STOP
600  REM SUBROUTINE TO APPLY KAISER WINDOW
610  REM AS IN PROGRAM 5.1

Sample run

VALUE OF N ? 20
NEED 21 FREQ SAMPLES:-
MODULUS OF SAMPLE 0 = ? 0
MODULUS OF SAMPLE 1 = ? 0.5
MODULUS OF SAMPLE 2 = ? 1.0
MODULUS OF SAMPLE 3 = ? 1.5
                :
MODULUS OF SAMPLE 12 = ? 6.0
MODULUS OF SAMPLE 13 = ? 6.5
MODULUS OF SAMPLE 14 = ? 0
                :
MODULUS OF SAMPLE 20 = ? 0
OK
FIR FLTR ORDER (EVEN) : ? 14
LINEAR QR QUAD PHASE (L OR Q) ? Q
ENTER ALPHA : ? 3
```

```
COEFFICIENTS ARE:-
A0:-0.02618
A1:0.12859
A2:-0.11764
A3:-0.18430
A4:0.57870
A5:-0.33381
A6:-1.89124
A7:0
A8:1.89124
A9:0.33381
A10:-0.57869
A11:0.18430
A12:0.11764
A13:-0.12859
A14:0.02618
```

Program Notes

(1) The user must supply a sufficiently large value of N, and $N + 1$ samples of the target gain response at frequencies $0, f_0, 2f_0, \ldots, Nf_0$ Hz where f_0 is the sampling frequency in Hertz divided by $2N + 1$. The order, M, of the required FIR filter must be an even number less than or equal to $2N$.

(2) The phase response is calculated automatically by the program. Linear or quadrature phase may be selected as in Program 5.1. A phase shift of $-(M/2)\omega$ radians is included in each sample of the phase response to delay the impulse response by $M/2$ sampling intervals before truncation.

(3) A Kaiser window is applied to the truncated impulse response. Its value of ALPHA (α) must be supplied.

(4) The sample run designs a 14th order lowpass differentiator with cut-off frequency at one third of the sampling frequency, i.e. $\omega = 2\pi/3$ radians/sample, and a choice of $\alpha = 3$ for the Kaiser window. Samples of the target gain response are derived from Figure 5.8. The target phase response is quadrature with a phase delay of seven sampling intervals.

5.7 Optimum FIR digital filter design

The two approximation methods for FIR digital filter design which have been discussed are simple and convenient to use. However the filters they produce are unlikely to be optimum in terms of commonly-adopted performance criteria, and much better filters can generally be designed by more sophisticated techniques. To illustrate by referring again to the target gain response in Figure 5.8, attempting to realize the sudden transition from 6.5 to 0 between samples 13 and 14 leads to relatively poor stopband attenuation for frequencies above $2\pi/3$ radians/sample. If stopband attenuation is considered to be important, a better lowpass differentiating filter may be obtained by choosing some intermediate gain for sample 14, say 3. The user may run Program 5.2 several times, with different gains at sample 14, to try and improve the filter. The effect of varying other gains in the transition between passband and stopband may also be investigated. Iterative techniques based on this approach are available [References 1,2] for designing optimised FIR digital filters, and more sophisticated techniques are also available (References 1,2,5).

5.8 Realization of FIR digital filters

FIR digital filters are often realized in the direct form illustrated in Figure 5.1. Programs 3.1 and 3.4 are based on this signal flow graph and DSP microprocessor programs or dedicated hardware may be developed along similar lines. There are, however, many alternative signal flow graphs, some of which have important advantages for particular implementations. It is also possible to realize an FIR digital filter using an FFT algorithm (see Chapter 6).

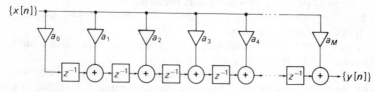

Figure 5.10 FIR filter in 'transpose form'

A useful alternative to the direct form in Figure 5.1 is the 'transpose' form illustrated in Figure 5.10. This is sometimes preferred in hardware implementations because all the multiplier inputs are identical. Its behaviour as a BASIC program would be identical to Program 3.3. Implementing linear or quadrature phase FIR filters may be simplified by taking advantage of the fact that the impulse responses of these filters have even or odd symmetry about the centre, as was pointed out in Section 5.4. For an even order linear phase filter, $a_0 = a_m$, $a_1 = a_{m-1}$, etc. and therefore Figure 5.1 may be rearranged as shown in Figure 5.11. The use of subtractors in place of some of the adders would allow a quadrature phase FIR filter to be similarly rearranged.

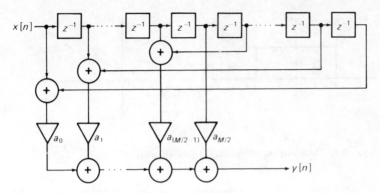

Figure 5.11 Alternative form for linear phase FIR filter

5.9 Introduction to IIR digital filter design

Many design techniques for IIR digital filters have adopted ideas and terminology developed for analogue filters and are implemented by transforming the transfer functions (see Appendix) of analogue 'prototype' filters into the system functions of digital filters with similar characteristics. Two such techniques are known as the 'impulse invariance' method and the 'bilinear transformation' method. Before describing these methods, a brief survey of analogue filters is presented. This survey refers to a derivation of essential analogue system theory given in the Appendix.

5.9.1. Analogue filters

Analogue filters are also designed in two stages: an approximation stage to produce a realizable transfer function $H(s)$ whose frequency response $H(j\Omega)$ is equal to or close to some prescribed function of Ω, and a realization stage to produce the analogue circuit. Prescribed functions of Ω are generally expressed in polar form, the modulus $G(\Omega)$ and argument $\theta(\Omega)$ being the prescribed gain and phase response respectively. Such a function is shown graphically in Figures 5.12(a) and 5.12(b) and is referred to as an idealized lowpass frequency response with cut-off frequency 1 radians/second and phase delay k. If a filter could be designed with $H(j\Omega)$ equal to this prescribed function, its output signal would be a delayed version of the input signal with all frequency components above 1 radians/second removed.

Many useful functions of Ω, including the idealized lowpass frequency response referred to above can only be approximated

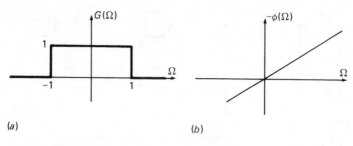

Figure 5.12 Ideal lowpass responses: (a) gain, (b) phase

by realizable transfer functions $H(s)$ evaluated at $s = j\Omega$. To be realizable by a causal stable filter, $H(s)$ must be a ratio of polynomials in s, as in Equation (A.11), with poles on the left hand side of the s plane. Since $H(j\Omega) = G(\Omega)\,e^{j\theta(\Omega)}$ and $H(-j\Omega) = G(\Omega)\,e^{-j\theta(\Omega)}$:

$$G(\Omega)^2 = H(s)H(-s) \text{ when } s = j\Omega \qquad (5.16)$$

and:

$$e^{2j\theta(\Omega)} = H(s)/H(-s) \text{ when } s = j\Omega \qquad (5.17)$$

By Equation (A.18):

$$H(s)\,H(-s) = K^2\,\frac{(z_1^2 - s^2)(z_2^2 - s^2)\ldots(z_N^2 - s^2)}{(p_1^2 - s^2)(p_2^2 - s^2)\ldots(p_M^2 - s^2)} \qquad (5.18)$$

where $z_1, z_2, \ldots, z_N$ and $p_1, p_2, \ldots, p_M$ are the zeros and poles of $H(s)$. A similar expression may be written for $H(s)/H(-s)$.

In general, the problem of choosing $H(s)$ such that $G(\Omega)$ and $\theta(\Omega)$ approximate some arbitrary gain and phase function can be quite complicated, requiring the use of optimization techniques beyond the scope of this book. However an important class of filters may be designed more simply. Consider the idealized lowpass gain response illustrated in Figure 5.12(a). The following approximations to this gain response are commonly used.

5.9.2 Butterworth approximation

$$G(\Omega) = \frac{1}{\sqrt{(1 + \Omega^{2n})}} \qquad (5.19)$$

This approximation produces the gain responses illustrated in Figure 5.13 for three different values of n. In all cases $G(0) = 1$

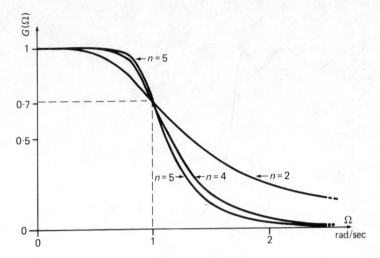

Figure 5.13 Butterworth-type lowpass gain responses

(i.e. 0 dB), $G(1) = 1/\sqrt{2}$ (i.e. -3 dB) and for values of Ω considerably greater than 1, $G(\Omega) \simeq (1/\Omega)^n$ (i.e. $-20n\log_{10}(\Omega)$ dB). Therefore, $G(2) \simeq -20n\log_{10}(2) \simeq -6n$ dB, $G(4) \simeq -12n$ dB, etc., and this illustrates that when $\Omega \gg 1$, a doubling of frequency causes a reduction of $6n$ dB in the gain. At $\Omega = 0$ and $\Omega = \infty$, $G(\Omega)$ is said to be 'maximally flat up to order n' since $d^k G(\Omega)/d\Omega^k = 0$ for all values of k up to and including n. This means that the gradient of the gain response graph is zero at $\Omega = 0$ and $\Omega = \infty$ and the gradient of the gradient is zero if $n \geqslant 2$ and so on.

5.9.3 Chebychev approximation

$$G(\Omega) = \frac{1}{\sqrt{\{1 + (\varepsilon V_n(\Omega))^2\}}} \tag{5.20}$$

where:

$$V_n(\Omega) = \cos\left[n\cos^{-1}(\Omega)\right] \tag{5.21}$$

and ε is a constant that may be chosen by the designer. Choosing $\varepsilon = 0.5$ when $n = 5$ produces the gain response illustrated in Figure 5.14. The general features of Chebychev-type approximations may be explained by observing that for values of Ω in the range -1 to 1, $V_n(\Omega)$ is the cosine of a real angle in the range 0 to $n\pi$. Therefore when $|\Omega| < 1$, $V_n(\Omega)$ has a maximum value of $+1$,

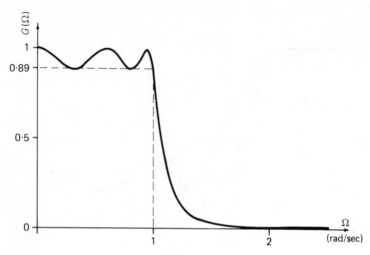

Figure 5.14 Chebychev lowpass gain response

a minimum value of -1 and causes the graph of $G(\Omega)$ against Ω to vary 'in equi-ripple fashion' between 1 (i.e. 0 dB); and $1/\sqrt{(1+\varepsilon^2)}$ (i.e. $-10\log_{10}(1+\varepsilon^2)$ dB which may be approximated by $-4.3\varepsilon^2$ dB when $\varepsilon < 1$). When $|\Omega| > 1$, $n\cos^{-1}(\Omega)$ becomes complex but it may be shown that:

$$\cos(n\cos^{-1}\Omega) = \tfrac{1}{2}[\{\Omega + \sqrt{(\Omega^2 - 1)}\}^n + \{\Omega + \sqrt{(\Omega^2-1)}\}^{-n}]$$

(5.22)

and this formula may be used to calculate $V_n(\Omega)$ without recourse to complex numbers. It follows that when Ω is considerably greater than 1, $\cos(n\cos^{-1}\Omega) \simeq 2^{n-1}\Omega^n$ and therefore $G(\Omega) \simeq (1/\Omega)^n/(2^{n-1}\varepsilon)$ (i.e. $-20n\log_{10}(\Omega) - 20\log_{10}(2^{n-1}\varepsilon)$ dB) when $|\Omega|$ is considerably greater than 1.

5.9.4. Elliptic approximation

$$G(\Omega) = \frac{1}{\sqrt{[1 + \varepsilon^2 R_{n,A}^2(\Omega)]}}$$

(5.23)

where ε is a constant and $R_{n,A}(\Omega)$ is an nth order 'Chebychev rational function' with properties which depend on the choice of a constant A. These properties are as follows:

(1) $R_{n,A}(\Omega)$ is a ratio of nth order polynomials in Ω with $R_{n,A}(-\Omega) = R_{n,A}(\Omega)$.

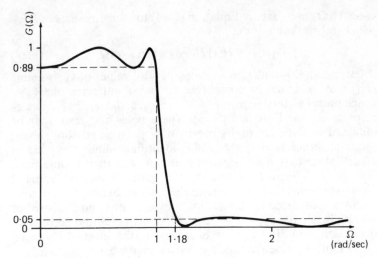

Figure 5.15 Elliptical lowpass gain response

(2) $R_{n,A}(\Omega)$ lies between -1 and 1 when $|\Omega| \leqslant 1$.

(3) $|R_{n,A}(\Omega)| \geqslant A$ for $|\Omega| \geqslant L_{n,A}$ where $L_{n,A}$ is a constant which depends on n and A.

Elliptic lowpass approximations are equi-ripple between 1 (i.e. 0 dB) and $1/\sqrt{(1+\varepsilon^2)}$ ($\simeq -4.3\varepsilon^2$ dB if $\varepsilon < 1$) when $|\Omega| \leqslant 1$ and are equi-ripple between zero (i.e. $-\infty$ dB) and $1/(\varepsilon A)$ (i.e. $-20\,(\log_{10}\varepsilon + \log_{10}A)$ dB) when $|\Omega| \geqslant L_{n,A}$ as illustrated in Figure 5.15 where $n = 4$, $A = 40$ and $\varepsilon = 0.5$ (giving a 0.97 dB passband ripple and a minimum stopband attenuation of about 26 dB). For a given value of A, the higher the value of n, the closer $L_{n,A}$ will be to 1, and the sharper will be the transition between passband ($|\Omega| \leqslant 1$) and stopband ($|\Omega| \geqslant L_{n,A}$). The higher the value of ε, the greater will be the stopband attenuation, but the higher will be the level of passband ripple. A general formula for $R_{n,A}(\Omega)$ cannot be conveniently given here, but a program for generating $H(s)$ for elliptic lowpass approximations will be presented in Section 5.9.8. Elliptic approximations are used to achieve much sharper passband to stopband transitions than are obtainable with Butterworth or Chebychev approximations of the same order.

5.9.5 Deriving H(s)

Many other gain response approximations may be proposed with a variety of different properties, advantages and disadvantages. In all cases $G(\Omega)$ must satisfy Equation (5.16) for some realizable $H(s)$, which means that:

$$G(s/\text{j})^2 = H(s)\,H(-s) \text{ when } s = \text{j}\Omega \qquad (5.24)$$

Extending this equation to encompass all values of s, a suitable $H(s)$ may be found by computing the poles and zeros of $G(s/\text{j})^2$ which must be equal to $\pm p_1, \pm p_2, \ldots, \pm p_M$ and $\pm z_1, \pm z_2, \ldots, \pm z_N$ respectively, by Equation (5.18). These poles and zeros may be obtained analytically or by means of a polynomial root-solving program. Poles of $H(s)$ are readily identified among the poles of $G(s/\text{j})^2$ since they have negative real parts and their counterparts $-p_1, -p_2, \ldots, -p_M$ have positive real parts. In general, zeros of $H(s)$ may be located anywhere in the s plane, but for the approximations considered in this section they are either non-existent or purely imaginary, as will be seen. Once its poles and zeros have been identified $H(s)$ may be expressed in the form of Equation (A.18) with K chosen to scale the maximum passband gain to unity.

5.9.6 $H(s)$ for Butterworth approximation

For the nth order Butterworth approximation (5.19) poles of $G(s/\text{j})^2$ occur when:

$$(s/\text{j})^{2n} = -1 = e^{(2k-1)\text{j}\pi}$$

i.e.

$$s = \text{j}e^{(2k-1)\text{j}\pi/2n}$$

$$= -\sin\left[(2k-1)\,\pi/2n\right] + \text{j}\cos\left[(2k-1)\pi/2n\right] \qquad (5.25)$$

for any integer k. Distinct poles with negative real parts are obtained when $k = 1, 2, \ldots, n$ and these are the poles of $H(s)$. There are no zeros. Combining complex conjugate pole pairs and scaling to make $|H(0)| = 1$, it may be shown that:

$$H(s) = \frac{1}{(1+s)^l \prod_{k=1}^{[n/2]} \{1 + 2\sin\left[(2k-1)\,\pi/2n\right]s + s^2\}} \text{ (Butterworth)} \qquad (5.26)$$

where $[n/2]$ is the integer part of $n/2$ and $l = 0$ when n is even and $l = 1$ when n is odd. Program 5.3 is based on this equation.

Program 5.3 BUTT: $H(s)$ for Butterworth lowpass filter (C/O 1 rad/sec)

```
10   REM BUTT:H(s) FOR LP FILTER;C/O 1 RAD/SEC
20   PRINT"ORDER";:INPUT N
30   M=INT(N/2):L=1-N+2*M
```

```
40   FOR K=L TO M
50   B0=1 : B1=1 : B2=0
60   IF K>0 THEN B1=2*SIN((2*K-1)*PI/2/N)
70   IF K>0 THEN B2=1
80   PRINT"SECTION: ";K
90   PRINT"A0: 1","B0: 1"
100  PRINT"A1: 0","B1: ";B1
110  PRINT"A2: 0","B2: ";B2
120  NEXT K
Sample run

ORDER? 4
SECTION: 1
A0: 1 B0: 1
A1: 0 B1: 0.76537
A2: 0 B2: 1
SECTION: 2
A0: 1 B0: 1
A1: 0 B1: 1.84776
A2: 0 B2: 1
```

5.9.7 $H(s)$ For Chebychev approximation

For the nth order Chebychev approximation (5.20), poles of $G(s/j)^2$ occur when:

$$j/\varepsilon = \pm \cos(n\cos^{-1}(s/j)) = \sin(n\cos^{-1}(s/j) + (2k-1)\pi/2)$$

for any integer value of k. Therefore, at each pole:

$$s = j \cos[(1/n)\sin^{-1}(j/\varepsilon) - (2k-1)\,\pi/2n]$$
$$= -\mu \sin[(2k-1)\,\pi/2n] + j\lambda \cos[(2k-1)\,\pi/2n] \qquad (5.27)$$

where:

$$\mu = -j \sin[(1/n)\sin^{-1}(j/\varepsilon)] = \sinh[(1/n)\sinh^{-1}(1/\varepsilon)] \quad (5.28)$$

and:

$$\lambda = \cos[(1/n)\sin^{-1}(j/\varepsilon)] = \sqrt{(1+\mu^2)}$$

Distinct poles with negative real parts are obtained when $k = 1, 2, ..., n$ and these are the poles of $H(s)$. There are no zeros. Combining complex conjugate pole pairs and scaling to ensure that $|H(j\Omega)| = 1$ when $\Omega = 0$ (strictly speaking, this should be $1/\sqrt{(1:\varepsilon^2)}$ when n is even):

$$H(s) = \frac{1}{(1+s/\mu)^l \displaystyle\prod_{k=1}^{[n/2]} (1 + 2\mu s_k s/u_k + s^2/u_k^2)} \text{(Chebychev)} \qquad (5.29)$$

where l and $[n/2]$ are as defined previously, $s_k = \sin\left[(2k-1)\,\pi/2n\right]$ and $u_k = \mu^2 + 1 - s_k^2$. Program 5.4 is based on this equation.

Program 5.4 CHEB: $H(s)$ for Chebychev lowpass filter (C/O 1 rad/ sec)

```
 10  REM:CHEB:H(S) FOR 1 RAD/S LP FILTER
 20  PRINT"ORDER";:INPUT N
 30  PRINT"PASSBAND RIPPLE(DB)";:INPUT R
 40  M=INT(N/2) : L=1-N+2*M
 50  E=SQR(10^(R/10)-1)
 60  MU=(1/E+SQR(1+1/E/E))^(1/N)
 70  MU=(MU-1/MU)/2
 80  FOR K=L TO M
 90  B0=1 : B1=1/MU : B2=0
100  SK=SIN((2*K-1)*PI/2/N)
110  IF K>0 THEN B2=1/(MU*MU+1-SK*SK)
120  IF K>0 THEN B1=2*MU*SK*B2
130  PRINT"SECTION: ";K
140  PRINT"A0: 1","B0: 1"
150  PRINT"A1: 0","B1: ";B1
160  PRINT"A2: 0","B2: ";B2
170  NEXT K
```

```
Sample run

ORDER? 5
PASSBAND RIPPLE(DB)? 0.97
SECTION: 0
A0: 1 B0: 1
A1: 0 B1: 3.4169
A2: 0 B2: 0
SECTION: 1
A0: 1 B0: 1
A1: 0 B1: 0.1827
A2: 0 B2: 1.00994
SECTION: 2
A0:1 B0: 1
A1:0 B1: 1.0983
A2:0 B2: 2.3194
```

Program note

As $\sinh(x) = (e^x - e^{-x})/2$ and $\sinh^{-1}(x) = \ln\left[x + \sqrt{(x^2+1)}\right]$ it follows that:

$$\mu = \left[\{1/\varepsilon + \sqrt{(1 + 1/\varepsilon^2)}\}^{1/n} - \{1/\varepsilon^2 + \sqrt{(1 + 1/\varepsilon^2)}\}^{-1/n}\right]$$

5.9.8 $H(s)$ for Elliptic approximation

For the nth order elliptic approximation (5.31), poles and zeros cannot be conveniently given analytically. They may be obtained for reasonable values of ε, n, A and Ω_c by a method proposed by Darlington [Reference 6] and Lind [Reference 7]. Program 5.5 uses this method to derive $H(s)$.

Program 5.5 ELLIP: $H(s)$ for elliptical lowpass filter (C/O 1 rad/ sec)

```
10   REM:ELLIP:H(S) FOR LP FILTER C/O 1 RAD/SEC
20   DEF FNR(X)=INT(X*1E4+0.5)/1E4
30   DIM Z(10)
40   PRINT"PASSBAND RIPPLE(DB)";:INPUT R
50   INPUT"STOPBAND ATTEN(DB) ";:INPUT V
60   PRINT"ORDER OF LP FILTER";:INPUT N
70   E=SQR(10^(R/10)-1)
80   A=SQR(10^(V/10)-1)/E:Y=SQR(A):L=1
90   F=1/E+SQR(1+1/E/E)
100  Y=Y*Y+SQR(Y^4-1):F=2*F*Y:L=L+1
110  IF F<1E8 THEN F=F/2+SQR(F*F/4+1)
120  IF Y<1E8 THEN 100
130  Y=2*Y*Y:L=L+2
140  F=(Y/F+SQR(Y/F*Y/F+1))^(1/N)
150  Z(1)=0.5*(2*Y)^(2/N)
160  FOR I=2 TO L
170  Z(I)=SQR((Z(I-1)+1/Z(I-1))/2)
180  NEXT I:PRINT"L(N,A)="Z(L)^2:Z(L)=1
190  I=2*INT(N/2)+1-N:U=ATN(1)*I*2/N:R=F
200  IF I>0 THEN 250
210  PRINT"SECTN 0":PRINT"A0 = 1","B0 = 1"
220  FOR J=1 TO L:R=(R-1/R)/2/Z(J):NEXT J
230  PRINT"A1 = 0","B1 = ";FNR(-1/R)
240  PRINT"A2 = 0","B2 = 0
250  FOR I=1 TO INT(N/2)
260  PRINT"SECTN ";I
270  W=Z(1)/COS(PI*(2*I-1)/2/N)
280  FOR J=2 TO L:W=(W+1/W)/2/Z(J):NEXT J
290  T=PI*I/N-U:R=F*COS(T):S=F*SIN(T)
300  FOR J=1 TO L
310  T=R*R+S*S:R=(R-R/T)/(2*Z(J))
320  S=(S+S/T)/(2*Z(J))
330  NEXT J  :  T=R*R+S*S
340  PRINT"A0 = 1","B0 = 1"
350  PRINT"A1 = 0","B1 = ";FNR(-2*R/T)
360  PRINT"A2 = ";FNR(1/W/W),"B2 = ";FNR(1/T)
370  NEXT I
380  STOP

Sample run

PASSBAND RIPPLE(DB)? 0.97
STOPBAND ATTEN(DB)? 26
ORDER OF LP FILTER? 4
L(N,A)=1.1773
SECTN 1
A0 = 1 B0 = 1
A1 = 0 B1 = 1.6214
```

```
A2 = 0.6635 = 2.0579
SECTN 2
A0 = 1 B0 = 1
A1 = 0 B1 = 0.1436
A2 = 0.1723 B2 = 0.9912
```

5.9.9 Phase response

Each of the approximation methods presented in this section produces a transfer function $H(s)$ from a knowledge only of the required gain response $G(\Omega)$. Once $H(s)$ is known, the phase response may be calculated and is therefore predetermined by the magnitude response. For many applications, the phase response thus obtained will be acceptable either because it turns out to be reasonably close to a linear phase response over the frequency range of interest, or because the application is such that phase effects are considered of little importance. Where phase effects are important, techniques, beyond the scope of this book, are available for independently specifying the phase response (see Reference 8, for example).

5.9.10 Frequency band transformations

The following transformations (References 1,2) may be applied to any lowpass transfer function $H(s)$ with a cut-off frequency of 1 radian/second.

Lowpass: $\qquad\qquad\qquad s \rightarrow s/\Omega_c$

Replacing s by s/Ω_c in the expression for $H(s)$ scales the cut-off frequency from 1 radian/second to Ω_c.

Highpass: $\qquad\qquad\qquad s \rightarrow \Omega_c/s$ (5.30)

Replacing s by Ω_c/s in the expression for $H(s)$ produces a transfer function whose gain response approximates the ideal highpass gain response (cut-off Ω_c) as illustrated in Figure 5.16(a).

Bandpass: $\qquad\qquad s \rightarrow \dfrac{(s^2 + \Omega_l \Omega_u)}{s(\Omega_u - \Omega_l)}$ (5.31)

This transformation produces a transfer function whose gain response approximates the ideal bandpass gain response, with cut-off frequencies Ω_u and Ω_l, as illustrated in Figure 5.16(b).

Bandstop: $\qquad\qquad s \rightarrow \dfrac{s(\Omega_u - \Omega_l)}{(s^2 + \Omega_l \Omega_u)}$ (5.32)

The resulting gain response approximates the ideal bandstop gain response, cut-off Ω_u *and* Ω_l, as illustrated in Figure 5.16(c).

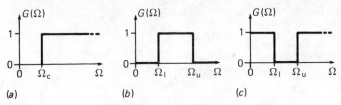

Figure 5.16 Ideal analogue gain responses: (a) highpass, (b) bandpass, (c) bandstop

The bandpass and bandstop transformations produce a fourth-order transfer function from each second order one in a cascade or parallel arrangement. These fourth order transfer functions are normally re-expressed as the product of two second-order transfer functions. Program 5.6 is provided for applying bandpass or bandstop transformations and carrying out the refactorization. Note that a serial cascade can be converted to a parallel arrangement using Program A.2 listed in the Appendix.

Program 5.6 BTRANS: Bandpass/stop transformations

```
 10 REM BTRANS: BANDPASS/STOP TRANSFORMATIONS
 20 PRINT"BP OR BS"; : INPUT T$
 30 PRINT"WL (RAD/SEC):"; : INPUT WL
 40 PRINT"WU (RAD/SEC):"; : INPUT WU
 50 P=WU*WL : D=WU-WL
 60 PRINT"ENTER COEFFS FOR A PROTOTYPE SECTN:-"
 70 PRINT"A0,A1,A2:"; : INPUT A0,A1,A2
 80 PRINT"B0,B1,B2:"; : INPUT B0,B1,B2
 90 PRINT"TRANSFORMED COEFFS:-"
100 IF A2<>0 THEN GOTO 150
105 IF B2<>0 THEN GOTO 150
110 IF T$<>"BS" THEN GOTO 130
120 T=A0 : A0=A1 : A1=T : T=B0 : B0=B1 : B1=T
130 E2=A1/D: E1=A0: E0=P*E2: G2=B1/D: G1=B0: G0=P*G2
140 PRINT : GOTO 210
150 GOSUB 250
160 D0=F0 : D1=F1 : D2=F2 : E0=G0 : E1=G1 : E2=G2
170 A0=B0 : A1=B1 : A2=B2 : GOSUB 250 : PRINT
180 PRINT"A0: ";D0," B0: ";F0
190 PRINT"A1: ";D1," B1: ";F1
200 PRINT"A2: ";D2," B2: ";F2 : PRINT
210 PRINT"A0: ";E0," B0: ";G0
220 PRINT"A1: ";E1," B1: ";G1
230 PRINT"A2: ";E2," B2: ";G2
240 PRINT : GOTO 60
250 IF T$<>"BS"THEN GOTO 270
260 T=A0 : A0=A2 : A2=T
270 F0=D*D*A0 : F1=0 : F2=0 : G0=0 : G1=0 : G2=1
```

```
280 IF A2<>0 THEN GOTO 310
290 IF A1=0 THEN RETURN
300 F0=0 : G0=P : F1=A1*D : G1=A0/F1 : RETURN
310 R=-A1/A2/2 : I=R*R-A0/A2 : F2=A2
320 IF I<0 THEN GOTO 350
330 F1=-(R+SQR(I))*F2 : F0=P*F2 : G0=P
340 G1=-R+SQR(I) : RETURN
350 T=2*P*A2+A0*D*D/2
360 M=SQR(T+SQR(T*T-P*A1*A1*D*D))
370 A=-A1*D/M : R=(M+SQR(M*M-4*P*A2))/2
380 F0=R*R : F1=-A*R : G0=P*P/R/R : G1=-A*P/R
390 RETURN
```

Sample run

```
BP OR BS? BP
WL (RAD/SEC):? 0.828
WU (RAD/SEC):? 2
ENTER COEFFS FOR A PROTOTYPE SECTN:-
A0,A1,A2:?1,0,0
B0,B1,B2:?1,1.414,1
TRANSFORMED COEFFS:-
A0: 1.373584 B0: 3.21700338
A1: 0          B1: 1.09403654
A2: 0          B2: 1

A0: 0          B0: 0.852450456
A1: 0          B1: 0.563171464
A2: 1          B2: 1


ENTER COEFFS FOR A PROTOTYPE SECTN:-
A0,A1,A2:?
Escape at line 70
```

5.10 IIR digital filter design by the impulse invariance technique

Given the transfer function $H_a(s)$ for an analogue prototype filter, this technique aims to transform it into the system function for a stable IIR digital filter with similar frequency response characteristics. The approach is an obvious one: to derive the impulse response $h_a(t)$ of the analogue filter and then to design a digital filter whose impulse response $\{h[n]\}$ is a sampled version of $h_a(t)$. This may be conveniently done by expressing $H_a(s)$ as a parallel arrangement of biquadratic transfer functions:

$$H_a(s) = \sum_{i=1}^{K+M} H_{ai}(s) \qquad (5.33)$$

where:

$$H_{ai}(s) = \frac{a_{0i} + a_{1i}s}{b_{0i} + b_{1i}s + b_{2i}s^2}$$

for each i. If $b_{2i} = 0$, then $b_{1i} \neq 0$ and $a_{1i} = 0$.

Such an expression for $H_a(s)$ may be obtained from a serial cascade by means of Program A.2 listed in the Appendix. Each $H_{ai}(s)$ may then be re-expressed as:

$$H_{ai}(s) = \frac{R_i}{(s-p_i)} + \frac{S_i}{(s-q_i)} \tag{5.35}$$

When $b_{2i} \neq 0$, p_i and q_i are the poles (assumed not identical) of $H_{ai}(s)$ and R_i, S_i are the residues (partial fraction coefficients) at these poles. When $b_{2i} = 0$, then $S_i = q_i = 0$.

By Equation (A.9), it may be shown that the Laplace transform of:

$$h_{ai}(t) = \begin{cases} R_i e^{p_i t} + S_i e^{q_i t} & t \geq 0 \\ 0 & t < 0 \end{cases} \tag{5.36}$$

is $H_{ai}(s)$ as defined by Equation (5.35) provided the real parts of p_i and q_i are negative. It follows that when $K=0$, the Laplace transform of:

$$h_a(t) = \sum_{i=1}^{M} h_{ai}(t) \tag{5.37}$$

is $H_a(s)$ as given by Equation (5.33), and $h_a(t)$ is the impulse response of the analogue prototype filter. Sampling $h_a(t)$ at intervals of T seconds gives the impulse response $\{h[n]\}$ where:

$$h[n] = \sum_{i=1}^{M} h_i[n] \tag{5.38}$$

with:

$$h_i[n] = h_{ai}(nT) = \begin{cases} R_i e^{p_i n T} + S_i e^{q_i n T} & n \geq 0 \\ 0 & n < 0 \end{cases} \tag{5.39}$$

The system function of the resulting digital filter is the z-transform of $\{h[n]\}$, i.e.:

$$H(z) = \sum_{i=1}^{M} H_i(z) \tag{5.40}$$

where:

$$\begin{aligned} H_i(z) &= \sum_{n-0}^{\infty} R_i e^{p_i n T} z^{-n} + \sum_{n-0}^{\infty} S_i e^{q_i n T} z^{-n} \\ &= \frac{R_i}{1-(e^{p_i T})\,z^{-1}} + \frac{S_i}{1-(e^{q_i T})\,z^{-1}} \end{aligned} \tag{5.41}$$

by summing geometric series, assuming $|e^{p_iT}z^{-1}| < 1$ and $|e^{q_iT}z^{-1}| < 1$. These conditions are satisfied for all values of z with $|z| \geq 1$ since the real parts of p_iT and q_iT are negative. Combining the two terms on the right hand side of Equation (5.41):

$$H_i(z) = \frac{(R_i + S_i) - (R_i e^{q_iT} + S_i e^{p_iT}) z^{-1}}{1 - (e^{p_iT} + e^{q_iT}) z^{-1} + e^{(p_i + q_i)T} z^{-2}} \qquad (5.42)$$

5.10.1 Applying the impulse invariance transformation

Program 5.7 is presented below for carrying out the transformation for each parallel section $H_i(s)$ of $H_a(s)$ to produce a parallel section $H_i(z)$ of $H(z)$ by the impulse invariance method. To illustrate how this program may be used to design IIR digital filters, consider the problem of designing a lowpass filter with a cut-off frequency at one fifth of the sampling frequency, i.e. at a relative frequency of $2\pi/5$. If the sampling frequency is assumed for convenience to be 1 Hz, thus making the sampling interval T equal to 1 second, the required cut-off frequency is 0.2 Hz or 1.2566 radians/second. The transfer function $H_a(s)$ for a fourth order Butterworth-type analogue lowpass filter with a cut-off frequency of 1.2566 radians/second may be obtained in parallel form as follows:

(1) Run Program 5.3 to obtain the fourth order normalized Butterworth transfer function:

$$H_a(s) = \left(\frac{1}{1 + 0.765s + s^2} \right) \left(\frac{1}{1 + 1.848s + s^2} \right) \qquad (5.43)$$

(2) Convert $H_a(s)$ into parallel form using Program A.2 (See Appendix) to obtain

$$H_a(s) = \left(\frac{-0.7071 - 0.9239s}{1 + 0.765s + s^2} \right) + \left(\frac{1.7071 + 0.9239s}{1 + 1.848s + s^2} \right) \qquad (5.44)$$

(3) Replace s by $s/1.2566$ to obtain

$$H_a(s) = \left(\frac{-0.7071 - 0.7352s}{1 + 0.6091s + 0.6333s^2} \right)$$

$$+ \left(\frac{1.7071 + 0.7352s}{1 + 1.4704s + 0.6333s^2} \right) \qquad (5.45)$$

When Program 5.7 is run for each parallel section of $H_a(s)$, the

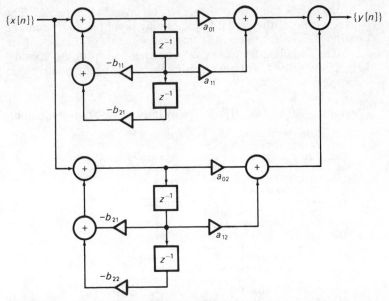

Figure 5.17 Fourth-order IIR filter in parallel form

following system function is obtained:

$$H(z) = \frac{-1.1610 + 0.0133z^{-1}}{1 - 0.4927z^{-1} + 0.3822z^{-2}}$$

$$+ \frac{1.1610 + 0.08369z^{-1}}{1 - 0.5553z^{-1} + 0.0981z^{-2}} \qquad (5.46)$$

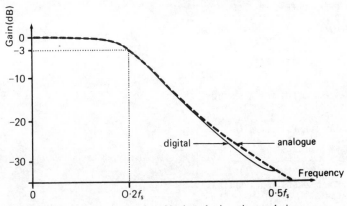

Figure 5.18 Gain response produced by impulse invarient technique

A signal flow graph for realizing $H(z)$ is given in Figure 5.17. The gain response of the digital filter, as may be obtained by running Program 3.5, is illustrated and compared with that of $H_a(s)$ in Figure 5.18. The sampling frequency may be changed from the nominal 1 Hz to any value f_s without affecting the shape of the relative gain response.

Program 5.7 IMPINV: IIR design by impulse invariance method

```
10    REM :IMPINV: IMPULSE INVARIANCE
20    PRINT"ENTER T:"; : INPUT T
30    PRINT"ENTER COEFFS FOR A SECTION:-"
40    PRINT" A0,A1: ";:INPUT A0,A1
50    PRINT"B0,B1,B2";:INPUT B0,B1,B2
60    IF B2<>0 THEN GOTO 80
70    Q=0:S=0:P=-B0/B1:R=A0/B1:GOTO 120
80    U=-B1/B2/2:V=U*U-B0/B2
90    IF V<0 THEN GOTO 150
100   V=SQR(V):P=U+V:Q=U-V:S=(P-Q)*B2
110   R=(A0+A1*P)/S:S=-(A0+A1*Q)/S
120   B1=-EXP(P*T)-EXP(Q*T):B2=EXP((P+Q)*T)
130   A0=R+S:A1=-R*EXP(Q*T)-S*EXP(P*T)
140   GOTO 190
150   V=SQR(-V):RR=A1/B2/2:RI=-(A0+U*A1)/V/B2/2
160   B1=-2*EXP(U*T)*COS(V*T)  :  B2=EXP(2*U*T)
170   A0=2*RR
180   A1=-2*EXP(U*T)*(RR*COS(V*T)+RI*SIN(V*T))
190   PRINT"TRANSFORMED COEFFS ARE:-"
200   PRINT"A0: ";A0," B0: 1"
210   PRINT"A1: ";A1," B1: ";B1
220   PRINT"A2: 0"   ," B2: ";B2
230   PRINT : GOTO 30


      Sample run

ENTER T: ? 1
ENTER COEFFS FOR A SECTION:-
A0,A1: ?-0.7071, -0.7352
B0,B1,B2: ?1, 0.6091, 0.6333
TRANSFORMED COEFFS ARE:-
A0: -1.16098      B0: 1
A1: 0.013297      B1: -0.49266
A2: 0             B2: 0.38221

ENTER COEFFS FOR A SECTION:-
A0,A1: ?1.7071, 0.7352
B0,B1,B2: ?1, 1.4704, 0.6333
TRANSFORMED COEFFS ARE:-
A0: 1.16098       B0: 1
A1: 0.083687      B1: -0.55532
A2: 0             B2: 0.09808

ENTER COEFFS FOR A SECTION:-
A0,A1: ?
Escape at line 40
```

Program notes

(1) The program runs repeatedly for any number of parallel second order sections. First order sections may be entered by setting $B2 = A1 = 0$.

(2) The sample run designs an IIR digital filter whose impulse response is that of an fourth order Butterworth lowpass filter, with cut-off frequency scaled to 1.2566 radians/second, sampled at intervals of 1 second. The IIR digital filter is therefore lowpass with a relative cut-off frequency of 1.2566 radians/sample.

5.10.2 Effect of aliasing

The reasons for the differences observed in Figure 5.18 between the analogue and digital gain responses are important to understand as they determine which types of filter can and cannot be successfully designed by the impulse invariance technique. By the sampling theorem (see Chapter 4), the sequence $\{h[n]\}$ obtained by sampling $h_a(t)$ with Fourier transform $H_a(j\Omega)$ at intervals of T seconds has discrete-time Fourier transform $H(e^{j\omega})$ which is related to $H_a(j\Omega)$ as follows:

$$H(e^{j\omega}) = \frac{1}{T} \sum_{r=-\infty}^{\infty} H_a(j\omega/T + 2\pi rj/T) \qquad (5.47)$$

If $H_a(j\Omega)$ were bandlimited to $|\Omega| < \pi/T$, i.e. half the sampling frequency, $H(e^{j\omega})$ and $H_a(j\omega/T)$ would be identical in the range $-\pi < \omega < \pi$ except for a scaling by the constant multiplier $1/T$. In practice, $H_a(j\Omega)$ can never be perfectly bandlimited and the effect of aliasing as discussed in Chapter 4 is to cause a discrepancy between analogue and digital frequency responses. When the analogue filter is Butterworth or Chebychev lowpass or bandpass with cut-off frequency or frequencies well below π/T radians/second, $H_a(j\Omega)$ will be relatively small outside the range $|\Omega| < \pi/T$ and the impulse invariance method will produce a reasonably good digital filter with $H(e^{j\omega})$ close to $H_a(j\Omega)$ for $|\Omega| < \pi$. Note that K in Equation (5.33) will always be zero for such a filter. Elliptic lowpass and bandpass filters are not well suited to the technique since K will not be zero. Highpass and bandstop filters are also unsuitable for the same reason.

5.11 IIR digital filter design by the bilinear transformation technique

Given an analogue transfer function $H_a(s)$, the bilinear transformation produces a digital system function $H(z)$ by means of the following mapping from the s-plane to the z-plane:

$$s \to \frac{1 - z^{-1}}{1 + z^{-1}} \qquad (5.48)$$

This means that:

$$H(z) = H_a\left(\frac{1 - z^{-1}}{1 + z^{-1}} \right) \qquad (5.49)$$

which will be a ratio of polynomials in z^{-1}. If, for example:

$$H_a(s) = \frac{1}{b_0 + b_1 s} \qquad (5.50)$$

then:

$$H(z) = \frac{1}{b_0 + [b_1(1 - z^{-1})/(1 + z^{-1})]}$$
$$= \frac{1 + z^{-1}}{(b_0 + b_1) + (b_0 - b_1)\, z^{-1}} \qquad (5.51)$$

By a similar calculation, if:

$$H_a(s) = \frac{a_0 + a_1 s + a_2 s^2}{b_0 + b_1 s + b_2 s^2} \qquad (5.52)$$

then:

$$H(z) = \frac{(a_0 + a_1 + a_2) + 2(a_0 - a_2)\, z^{-1} + (a_0 - a_1 + a_2)\, z^{-2}}{(b_0 + b_1 + b_2) + 2(b_0 - b_2)\, z^{-1} + (b_0 - b_1 + b_2)\, z^{-2}} \qquad (5.53)$$

which can often be re-expressed in the form:

$$H(z) = K\left(\frac{1 + A_1 z^{-1} + A_2 z^{-2}}{1 + B_1 z^{-1} + B_2 z^{-2}} \right) \qquad (5.54)$$

5.11.1 Properties of the transformation

(1) The transfer function of a stable analogue filter of order N is transformed to the system function of a stable digital filter of the same order N.

(2) For any value of ω, the value of $H(e^{j\omega})$ is equal to $H_a(j\Omega)$ where:

$$\Omega = 1 \tan(\omega/2) \qquad (5.55)$$

A method of proving Property 1 is discussed in Problem (5.8).

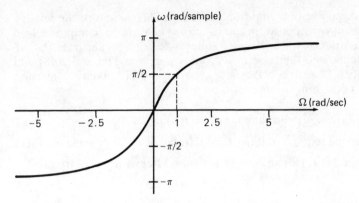

Figure 5.19 Frequency warping by bilinear transformation

Property 2 follows by showing that when $z = e^{j\omega}$:

$$\frac{1 - z^{-1}}{1 + z^{-1}} = \frac{e^{-j\omega/2}\left(e^{j\omega/2} - e^{-j\omega/2}\right)}{e^{-j\omega/2}\left(e^{j\omega/2} + e^{-j\omega/2}\right)}$$

$$= j\frac{\sin(\omega/2)}{\cos(\omega/2)} = j\tan(\omega/2)$$

and therefore $H(e^{j\omega}) = H_a(j\Omega)$ with $\Omega = \tan(\omega/2)$.

By property 2, the analogue frequency response for $\Omega = -\infty$ to ∞ is mapped to a relative frequency response for $\omega = -\pi$ to π by an inverse TAN function as illustrated in Figure 5.19. The mapping is almost linear for $-0.5 < \Omega < 0.5$ but becomes progressively more nonlinear or 'warped' as Ω is increased beyond this range, causing a wider range of analogue frequencies to be mapped to a smaller and

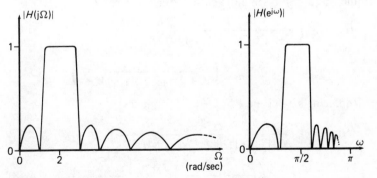

Figure 5.20 Effect of frequency warping

smaller range of digital frequencies. As $|\Omega|$ increases, the relative frequency response becomes more and more compressed in comparison to the analogue frequency response as illustrated by the analogue and digital gain responses shown in Figure 5.20(a) and 5.20(b). The effect of frequency warping must be taken into account when designing filters by this method.

5.11.2 *Design procedure for a low-pass digital filter*

Given the required relative cut-off frequency ω_c for the digital filter:

(1) Find $H_a(s)$ for an analogue lowpass filter with cut-off frequency

$$\Omega_c = \tan(\omega_c/2) \qquad (5.56)$$

(2) Replace s by $(1 - z^{-1})/(1 + z^{-1})$ in $H_a(s)$ to obtain H(z).

The choice of Ω_c as given by Equation (5.56) anticipates the frequency warping effect of the bilinear transformation and Ω_c is often called the 'pre-warped' cut-off frequency. The passband of the analogue filter is thus prearranged so that it becomes the passband of the required digital filter after the transformation even though the general shape of the gain and phase responses within the passband will be subject to a degree of warping. Clearly $H_a(j\Omega_c)$ will be equal to $H(e^{j\omega c})$ and $H_a(j\Omega)$ for $|\Omega| > \Omega_c$ will be mapped to $H(e^{j\omega})$ for $\omega_c < |\omega| < \pi$ which defines the stopband.

As an example, consider the design of a fourth order IIR lowpass filter, with $\omega_c = 2\pi/5$, from a Butterworth prototype. The fourth order prototype, with cut-off frequency 1 radian/second, may be obtained by running Program 5.3 and is approximately as given in Equation (5.43).

By Equation (5.56) the required pre-warped cut-off frequency is $\Omega_c = \tan(\pi/5) = 0.7265$ radians/second. Replacing s by s/Ω_c in Equation (5.43) to scale the cut-off frequency to Ω_c:

$$H_a(s) = \left(\frac{1}{1 + 1.0534s + 1.8944s^2} \right)$$

$$\times \left(\frac{1}{1 + 2.5432s + 1.8944s^2} \right) \qquad (5.57)$$

Replacing s by $(1 - z^{-1})/(1 + z^{-1})$ produces:

$$H(z) = \left(\frac{1 + 2z^{-1} + z^{-2}}{3.9478 - 1.7888z^{-1} + 1.841z^{-2}} \right)$$

$$\times \left(\frac{1 + 2z^{-1} + z^{-2}}{5.4376 - 1.7888z^{-1} + 0.3512z^{-2}} \right) \qquad (5.58)$$

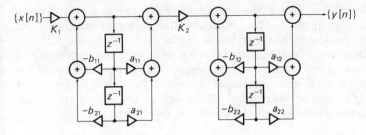

Figure 5.21 Fourth-order cascade

which may be re-expressed as:

$$0.2533 \left(\frac{1 + 2z^{-1} + z^{-2}}{1 - 0.4531z^{-1} + 0.4663z^{-2}} \right)$$

$$\times (0.1839) \left(\frac{1 + 2z^{-1} + z^{-2}}{1 - 0.329z^{-1} + 0.0645z^{-2}} \right) \qquad (5.59)$$

$H(z)$ may be realized as a serial cascade of two 'Direct Form II' signal flow graphs as shown in Figure 5.21. Each section has a gain of one in the passband. Figure 5.22 shows the relative gain response of $H(z)$, and this may be compared with the gain response of $H_a(s)$ shown as a dashed line in Figure 5.18. The gains are equal at zero frequency and at the cut-off frequencies. Above the cut-off frequency, the effect of frequency warping is to compress the

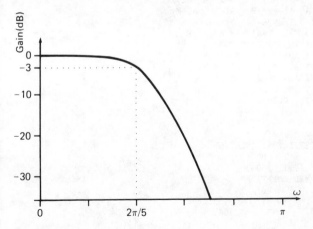

Figure 5.22 Gain response of lowpass filter designed by bilinear transformation

infinitely long 'tail' of the analogue frequency response into a finite frequency range and for a lowpass filter, this increases the cut-off rate. Comparing the solid line in Figure 5.18 with Figure 5.22, the bilinear transformation produces a significantly higher cut-off rate than was obtained for the same lowpass filter specification using the impulse invariance technique. However the effect of frequency warping can be undesirable in some applications, especially as the phase response as well as the gain response is affected.

5.11.3 Implementing the bilinear transformation

Program 5.8 is provided for applying the bilinear transformation to a biquadratic or first order transfer function $H_a(s)$, as represented by Equation (5.52), to produce $H(z)$ as represented by Equation (5.54). Serial or parallel arrangements of biquadratic or first order transfer functions may be transformed one section at a time.

Program 5.8 BILIN: bilinear transformation of biquadratic section

```
 10  REM:BILIN:  BILINEAR TRANSFORMATION
 20  PRINT"ENTER COEFFS FOR A SECTION:-"
 30  PRINT"A0,A1,A2: ";  : INPUT A0,A1,A2
 40  PRINT"B0,B1,B2: ";  : INPUT B0,B1,B2
 50  IF B2<>0 THEN GOTO 100
 60  IF A2<>0 THEN GOTO 100
 70  P=B0+B1 :  B1=(B0-B1)/P :  B0=1
 80  K=(A0+A1)/P : A1=(A0-A1)/P : A0=K
 90  GOTO 140
100  P=B0+B1+B2 :  Q=2*(B0-B2)/P
110  B2=(B0-B1+B2)/P :  B1=Q :  B0=1
120  K =(A0+A1+A2)/P :  Q=2*(A0-A2)/P
130  A2=(A0-A1+A2)/P :  A1=Q :  A0=K
140  IF K=0 THEN K=1
150  A0=A0/K :  A1=A1/K :  A2=A2/K
160  PRINT"TRANSFORMED COEFFS ARE:-"
170  PRINT"A0: ";A0," B0:  ";B0
180  PRINT"A1: ";A1," B1:  ";B1
190  PRINT"A2: ";A2," B2:  ";B2
200  PRINT" K: ";K
210  PRINT : GOTO 20

Sample run

ENTER COEFFS FOR A SECTION:-
A0,A1,A2: ? 1,0,0
B0,B1,B2: ? 1, 1.0534, 1.8944
TRANSFORMED COEFFS ARE:-
A0:  1         B0:   1
A1:  2         B1:   -0.4531
A2:  1         B2:   0.4663
 K:  0.2533
```

```
ENTER COEFFS FOR A SECTION:-
A0,A1,A2: ? 1, 0, 0
B0,B1,B2: ? 1, 2.5432, 1.8944
TRANSFORMED COEFFS ARE:-
A0:  1        B0:  1
A1:  2        B1:  -0.3290
A2:  1        B2:  0.0646
 K:  0.1839

ENTER COEFFS FOR A SECTION:-
A0,A1,A2: ?
Escape at line 30
```

Program notes

(1) The program runs repeatedly for any number of sections. For first order sections enter B2 and A1 as zero.

(2) The sample run transforms two serial sections of $H_a(s)$ for a fourth-order Butterworth lowpass filter with cut-off frequency scaled to $\tan(\omega_c/2)$ with $\omega_c = 2\pi/5$ into two serial sections of $H(z)$ as given in Equation (5.59).

(3) A parallel realization of $H(z)$ may be obtained by submitting $H_a(s)$ as defined by Equation (5.43) to Program A.2 before applying the bilinear transformation or alternatively by submitting $H(z)$ as defined by Equation (5.58). Parallel realizations are sometimes easier to program in fixed point arithmetic.

5.11.4 Bandpass and bandstop filter design

A bandpass IIR digital filter with relative lower and upper cut-off frequencies ω_l and ω_u may be designed by transforming an analogue bandpass filter obtained as described in Section 5.8. The frequency warping effect must be taken into account when designing the analogue filter. This simply means that both cut-off frequencies must be pre-warped. Consider the design of a fourth order Butterworth-derived bandpass filter with lower and upper cut-off frequencies $\omega_l = \pi/4$ and $\omega_u = \pi/2$ radians per sample. A fourth order analogue bandpass filter is required with the following prewarped cut-off frequencies:

$$\Omega_l = \tan(\omega_l/2) = \tan(\pi/8) = 0.4142 \text{ radians/second}$$

$$\Omega_u = \tan(\omega_u/2) = \tan(\pi/4) = 1 \text{ radian/second}$$

This may be obtained by running Program 5.6 to apply the bandpass transformation (5.31) to the normalized second order

Butterworth transfer function:

$$H(s) = \frac{1}{1 + 1.4142s + s^2} \tag{5.60}$$

which may be obtained by running Program 5.3. The following transfer function is obtained:

$$H(s) = \left(\frac{0.3432}{0.8042 + 0.5468s + s^2}\right)\left(\frac{s^2}{0.2133 + 0.2816s + s^2}\right) \tag{5.61}$$

Applying the transformation to each section (using Program 5.8) we obtain:

$$H(z) = 0.146\left(\frac{1 + 2z^{-1} + z^{-2}}{1 - 0.1666z^{-1} + 0.5348z^{-2}}\right)$$

$$\times (0.669)\left(\frac{1 - 2z^{-1} + z^{-2}}{1 - 1.0525z^{-1} + 0.6232z^{-2}}\right) \tag{5.62}$$

which may be realized by the signal flow graph shown in Figure 5.21. Its gain response is shown in Figure 5.23.

This technique may be used to design bandpass filters of any order, and highpass and bandstop filters may similarly be designed with the aid of analogue frequency band transformations as described in Section 5.9.10. As the whole of the analogue frequency response is mapped to relative frequencies in the range $-\pi$ to π, the bilinear transformation does not suffer from the aliasing problems encountered with the impulse invariance technique. Any type of

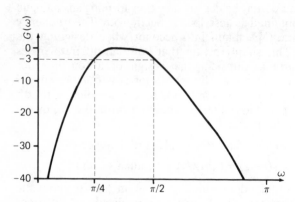

Figure 5.23 Band-pass gain response by bilinear transformation

analogue lowpass prototype may be used, including Chebychev and elliptical which offer a compromise between passband ripple and cut-off rate. As seen in the preceding theory, the level of passband and stopband ripple will be unaffected by the bilinear transformation, but the frequency response shape and therefore the cut-off rate will be affected.

5.12 Implementation in finite word-length fixed point arithmetic

Real time implementations of digital filters often use fixed point two's complement arithmetic as discussed in Chapter 1. To implement the filters designed in this chapter in fixed point arithmetic, a strategy must be devised for representing coefficient values and signal samples in binary form with a binary point assumed at a suitable position within each binary number. Some care is needed as the wordlength available is finite and the designer will wish to make maximum use of the available bits to minimize the effects of quantisation error without incurring distortion due to overflow.

It is convenient to refer to a fixed point binary number with n bits after the binary point as having 'Qn' format. Integers are therefore in Q0 format and an example of a sixteen bit number in Q12 format is:

$$0101.010101010101 \simeq 5.333$$

The position of the binary point determines the range of numbers that can be stored without overflow and the precision to which a given number within the range is represented. For example, a sixteen bit Q12 format accommodates numbers in the range -8 to $+8$ with a precision equivalent to between three and four decimal digits after the decimal point. A useful 'rule of thumb' is that ten binary places are equivalent to about three decimal places.

When implementing digital filters in fixed point arithmetic, it is useful to note that:

(1) The Q format remains unchanged after the addition or subtraction of two Qn numbers. Quantisation errors are not incurred, but overflow can occur when the sum of two numbers becomes too large in magnitude for the available wordlength. Overflow effectively adds a large positive or negative constant to the true result of an addition or subtraction and causes the sum of two positive numbers to appear negative, or the sum of two negative numbers to appear positive.

(2) Multiplication of a Qn number by a Qm number each of word-length l produces a Q$(m + n)$ number of wordlength up to 2l. Although the multiplication process itself cannot overflow or produce quantisation error, the wordlength of the result is normally reduced back to l bits thus incurring quantisation error. The reduction process if often done after the results of many multiplications have been added together.

(3) A fixed point digital processor keeps no record of Q formats and treats each number essentially as an integer. Processors can usually multiply and divide by powers of two very efficiently and this is useful for converting sample values from one Q format to another during processing. A Ql number may be converted to Q$(l + n)$ format simply by multiplying its binary representation by 2^n. If $n < 0$ this process incurs quantisation error due to truncation and if $n > 0$, overflow can occur.

(4) Given a decimal number, its Qn representation may be obtained by (a) multiplying the decimal number by 2^n, (b) rounding to the nearest integer, (c) converting the integer to binary form. Most microprocessor development systems will accept the integer obtained at step (b) and convert it automatically to binary. It is convenient to refer to this integer as the 'equivalent integer' for the fixed point number.

5.12.1 FIR filter example

Consider how an FIR digital filter as represented by the signal flow graph shown in Figure 5.1 could be implemented on a typical 16-bit fixed point digital signal processing device capable of (a) storing 16-bit numbers, (b) multiplying two 16-bit numbers (each representing an equivalent integer in the range -32768 to 32767) to produce a 32-bit two's complement number, (c) adding together 32-bit numbers, (d) efficiently multiplying and dividing by any power of two.

Such an FIR filter, of order ten, was designed in Section 5.2.1. Its eleven multiplier coefficients are the elements of the sequence (5.5). Since all multiplier coefficients are less than one in modulus, they may be represented as 16-bit words in Q15 format. Referring to A_i as the equivalent integer for a_i it follows that since $a_0 = 1/5\pi$, $A_0 = 2^{15}/5\pi = 2086$ when rounded to the nearest integer. Repeating this calculation for $a_{1, 2}, \ldots, a_{10}$, gives:

$$A_0 = A_{10} = 2086 \qquad (0.000100000100110)$$
$$A_2 = A_8 = -3477 \qquad (1.111001001101010)$$

$$A_4 = A_6 = 10430 \qquad (0.010100000111110)$$
$$A_5 = 16384 \qquad (0.1000000000000000)$$

with all other coefficients zero. The fixed point binary representation is given in brackets with the assumed position of the binary point shown. If the sixteen bit input signal is considered to be in Q14 format (e.g. to represent voltages in the range ± 2 volt), each multiplier in Figure 5.1 produces a 32-bit number in Q29 format. These 32-bit numbers may be added together and the result may then be scaled by 2^{-15} (thus incurring quantisation error) to produce a fixed point number in the same format (Q14) as the input. Overflow can occur during any of the double precision additions, effectively adding or subtracting a large number from the true result of the addition. Fortunately the gain of this particular filter is less than or equal to one at all frequencies and as the Q format of the output is the same as that of the input it is likely that the effect of any positive overflow will eventually be cancelled out by an equal negative overflow. Had the gain been significantly greater than one for any range of frequencies, the designer may have considered adopting a different Q format for the coefficients or possibly scaling down the input slightly.

The operation of a fixed point implementation of a digital filter may be verified in BASIC before it is committed to real time implementation. The BASIC program is written using equivalent integers to represent fixed point numbers in exactly the same way as they would be represented in the real time implementation. Any non-integers generated are rounded or truncated to integers and provision for simulating overflow conditions is also made. Program 5.9 is based on the example considered above.

Program 5.9 FIXFIR: simulation of FIR filter in fixed point

```
10 REM FIXFIR: FIR 16-BIT FIXED PT SIMULATION
20 DIM A(10),X1(10),X(100)
30 FOR I=0 TO 10 : READ A(I) : NEXT I
40 DATA 2086, 0, -3477, 0, 10430, 16384
50 DATA 10430, 0, -3477, 0, 2086
55 REM STORE 100 SAMPLES OF A VOLTAGE WAVEFORM IN ARRAY X:-
60 NS=100 : GOSUB 10000
70 PRINT"Q FORMAT FOR INPUT:"; : INPUT Q
80 PRINT"START SIMULATION:-"
90 FOR I=0 TO 10 : X1(I)=0 : NEXT I
100 MX=2^15 : MA=2^31
110 FOR N=0 TO NS-1 : XI=X(N)
120   XI=INT(XI*(2^Q)) : REM CONVERT TO EQUIV INTEGER
130   REM SIMULATE OVERFLOW(16-BIT WORD):-
140     IF XI>MX-1 THEN XI=XI-2^16
150     IF XI>MX-1 THEN GOTO 140
```

```
160    IF XI< -MX THEN XI=XI+2^16
170    IF XI< -MX THEN GOTO 160
180    AC = XI*A(0)
190    FOR I=0 TO 9
200    AC=AC+A(10-I)*X1(10-I) : X1(10-I)=X1(9-I)
210    REM SIMULATE OVERFLOW(32-BIT WORD):-
220        IF AC>MA-1 THEN AC=AC-2^32
230        IF AC>MA-1 THEN GOTO 220
240        IF AC< -MA THEN AC=AC+2^32
250        IF AC< -MA THEN GOTO 240
260    NEXT I : X1(1) = XI
270    REM CONVERT RESULT (IN AC) TO 16 BIT WORD Y:-
270    Y=INT(AC*(2^-15)) : REM INCURS QUANTISN ERROR
280    Y=Y/2^Q : REM CONVERT EQUIV INT IN Y TO VOLTAGE
290    PRINT"X(";N;")=";X(N)," Y(";N;")=";Y
300 NEXT N
310 END
10000 REM ARRAY DEFN SUBROUTINE(SEE PROGRAM 1.4, CHAPTER 1)
```

Sample run

```
SEQUENCE TYPE: SN
PERIODS OVER 100 SAMPLE: 5
NO. SAMPLES DELAY: 0
Q FORMAT FOR INPUT: 14
START OF SIMULATION:-
X(0)= 0          Y(0)= 0
X(1)= 0.3090     Y(1)= 0.0197
X(2)= 0.5878     Y(2)= 0.0374
X(3)= 0.8090     Y(3)= 0.0187
    .                .
    .                .
    .                .
X(99)=-0.3090  Y(99)=-0.9327
```

Program notes

(1) This program processes a 100 sample input sequence generated by subroutine 10000 by converting each sample to an equivalent integer and utilizing integer arithmetic. Integerized coefficient values (Q15) are read into array A. The effects of quantisation at accumulated multiplier outputs and possible overflows in 32-bit arithmetic are faithfully simulated. The possibility of input overflow is also simulated.

(2) The sample run gives the response of a fixed point implementation of the FIR filter designed in Section 5.2 to a sinusoidal input. If the output is compared with what would be produced by Program 3.3, the fixed point filter will show some discrepancies due to quantisation, but will normally be considered satisfactory.

5.12.2 IIR filter example

Now consider how an IIR biquadratic section with system function:

$$H(z) = \frac{1 - 1.33z^{-1} + 0.98z^{-2}}{1 - 1.28z^{-1} + 0.92z^{-2}} \qquad (5.63)$$

could be implemented using the fixed point processor as specified above. Multiplying the numerator and denominator of $H(z)$ by $2^{14} = 16384$, and rounding each coefficient of z^{-1} and z^{-2} to the nearest integer, $H(z)$ becomes:

$$H(z) = \frac{16384 - 21791z^{-1} + 16056z^{-1}}{16384 - 20972z^{-1} + 13271z^{-1}} \qquad (5.64)$$

$H(z)$ can now be realized by the signal flow graph in Figure 3.16(b) with $b_0 = a_0 = 16384$, $a_1 = -21791$, $a_2 = 16056$, $b_1 = -20972$ and $b_2 = 13271$. Implementation on the fixed point processor is now straightforward since all multipliers are integers (Q0) apart from the $1/b_0$ multiplier which divides by a power of two. Program 5.10 simulates this fixed point implementation in BASIC. The designer should be aware of certain difficulties that can arise using IIR digital filters in fixed point arithmetic and these may be illustrated by running Program 5.10.

Program 5.10 FIXIIR: simulation of IIR filter in fixed point

```
10 REM FIXIIR: IIR 16-BIT FIXED PT SIMULATION
20 READ A1,A2,B0,B1,B2
30 DATA -21791, 16056, 16384, -20972, 13271
40 PRINT"Q FORMAT FOR INPUT:"; : INPUT Q
50 REM START SIMULATION:-
60 W1=0 : W2=0 : MW=2^15
70 PRINT"X="; : INPUT XI
80 XI=INT(XI*(2^Q)) :REM INTEGERISE INPUT SAMPLE
90 AC=XI*B0-W1*B1-W2*B2
100 W=INT(AC/B0)
110 REM W IS 16-BIT. SIMULATE EFFECT OF OVERFLOW:-
120     IF W> MW-1 THEN PRINT"OVERFLOW+";
130     IF W> MW-1 THEN W=W-2^16
140     IF W> MW-1 THEN GOTO 130
150     IF W<-MW   THEN PRINT"OVERFLOW-";
160     IF W<-MW   THEN W=W+2^16
170     IF W<-MW   THEN GOTO 160
180 AC=AC + A1*W1 +A2*W2
190 Y=INT(AC/B0) :REM BACK TO 16-BITS
200 W2 = W1 : W1 = W
210 PRINT"   Y="; Y/2^Q :REM PRINT OUTPUT SAMPLE (AS VOLTAGE)
220 GOTO 70
```

```
Sample run 1

Q FORMAT FOR INPUT:? 10
X=? 0.5       Y=0.5
X=? 0.75      Y=0.7246
X=? 0         Y=0.0146
X=? 0         Y=0.1670
   .             .
   .             .
   .             .

Sample run 2

Q FORMAT FOR INPUT:? 15
X=? 0.5       Y=0.5
X=? 0.75    OVERFLOW+   Y= 0.7250
X=? 0       OVERFLOW-   Y= 0.1155
X=? 0       OVERFLOW+   Y=-0.1444
X=? 0       OVERFLOW-   Y= 0.1616
X=? 0       OVERFLOW+   Y=-0.1162
X=? 0       OVERFLOW-   Y= 0.1603
   .             .
   .             .
   .             .
```

Program notes

(1) This program implements the IIR filter whose system function is given by Equation (5.63). Overflow is most likely to occur at W in the signal flow graph illustrated in Figure 3.16(b) and this effect will be faithfully simulated. The possibility of other overflows is disregarded to simplify the program.

(2) Two sample runs are presented. The first run shows that the filter works reasonably well when Q10 format is chosen to represent the input signal, assumed to be in the range −1 to +1. Quantisation effects may be analysed by running Program 3.6 for the same system function and comparing the outputs.

(3) The second run selects Q15 format for the input, giving greater precision at the expense of larger equivalent integers. However, overflow occurs at W and this immediately gives rise to a catastrophic 'overflow limit cycle' behaviour which continues indefinitely. Such limit cycles must be avoided.

(4) To select a more suitable Q format for the input, it is necessary to predict how large the signal at W is likely to become. Under the assumption that any large input signals will be approximately sinusoidal, this prediction may be made by running Program 3.5 for:

$$H_1(z) = 1/(1 + 1.28z^{-1} + 0.92z^{-2})$$

which is the system function between the input and W. The maximum gain may be estimated, this being denoted by $G_1(\text{max})$.

For this example, $G_1(\text{max}) \simeq 16 \, (= 24 \, \text{dB})$. To avoid overflow at W, the range of equivalent integers produced at the input must be within $\pm 2^{15}/G_1(\text{max}) \simeq \pm 2^{11}$ in this case. For input signals in the range ± 1, this allows a Q format of up to Q11.

(5) It is often impossible or undesirable to eliminate the possibility of overflow completely. Fortunately, some processors provide an option known as 'saturation overflow mode' which produces the largest positive number when positive overflow occurs and the largest negative number when negative overflow occurs. The effect of saturation overflow mode may be simulated by replacing lines 130 and 160 in Program 5.10 by:

```
130 IF W>MW-1 THEN W=MW-1
160 IF W<-MW THEN W=-MW
```

Running this modified program for the data used in the second sample run demonstrates that overflow limit cycles may be eliminated using saturation overflow mode.

5.12.3 Effects of quantisation

Quantisation within a finite wordlength implementation of a digital filter causes two effects: (a) inaccuracies in frequency response due to coefficient quantisation; (b) noise in the filter output due to internal signal quantisation.

These effects add to the effect of quantising the input samples as discussed in Chapter 4. Other potentially more catastrophic effects can be observed if non-cancelling overflow errors are allowed to occur at summer outputs and these should be avoided or minimized by careful selection of fixed point formats as detailed in the previous sections.

The effects of coefficient quantisation on the frequency response of a digital filter may be analysed by means of Program 3.4 for FIR filters or Program 3.5 for IIR filters realized as cascades of second-order sections (see Problem 5.12). Other arrangements for IIR filters are rarely used as they often produce high coefficient sensitivity and unmanageable internal gains.

The effects of internal signal quantisation can be analysed as for input signal quantisation (see Chapter 4) and simulated in BASIC (see Programs 5.9 and 5.10). Quantisation noise is added at each point where rounding or truncation takes place, and such noise accumulates and is modified as it passes through the filter to appear at the output. When signals being processed become small in comparison to quantisation error, the effect of quantising unwanted internal signals which are themselves generated by quantisation can be significant. The effect is sometimes seen in IIR filters as 'small scale limit cycles' which are self-sustaining signals caused by quantisation combined with feedback (see Problem 5.13).

Programming in fixed point arithmetic involves a careful balance between the avoidance of overflow and the maximisation of signal levels to minimize the effect of rounding error. The overall effect of quantisation errors depends very much on the nature of the system being implemented, and general guidelines can at best be sketchy. A large amount of research has been carried out in this area and a useful bibliography may be found in Reference 9.

5.12.4 Comparison of IIR and FIR digital filters

For many specifications, either an IIR or an FIR filter may be used, and it is therefore important to compare these two types of filter.

IIR filters are generally more economical to implement requiring fewer delays, multipliers and summers than a broadly equivalent FIR filter. The disadvantages of IIR filters are that they can be more sensitive to coefficient round-off error and the possibility of overflow in fixed point arithmetic. These effects can lead to instability. An IIR filter cannot be perfectly linear phase.

FIR filters may be realized by nonrecursive structures which are simpler and more convenient for programming especially on devices specifically designed for digital signal processing. These structures are always stable, and because there is no recursion (feedback), round-off and overflow errors are easily controlled. An FIR filter can be linear phase. The main disadvantage of FIR filters are that large orders can be required to perform fairly simple filtering operations.

5.13 References

1. Rabiner, L. R. and Gold, B. (1975) *Theory and Application of Digital Signal Processing*, Prentice-Hall
2. Oppenheim, A. V. and Schafer, R. W. (1975) *Digital Signal Processing*, Prentice-Hall
3. Ziener, R. E., Tranter, H. W and Fannin, D. R. (1983) *Signals and Systems*, Macmillan
4. Williams, C. S. (1986) *Designing Digital Filters*, Prentice-Hall
5. *Programs for Digital Signal Processing*, IEEE Press (1979)
6. Darlington, S. (1978) Simple algorithms for elliptical filters and generalisations thereof. *IEEE Trans. Circuits and Systems*, CAS-25 no. 12, 975–980
7. Lind, L. F. (1984) Simple computation of elliptic function filters. *Digest of 1984 IEE Saraga Memorial Colloquium on Electrical Filters*, London, UK
8. Rhodes, J. D. (1976) *Theory of Electrical Filters*, Wiley
9. Antoniou, A. (1979) *Digital Filters: Analysis and Design*, McGraw-Hill

Problems

(5.1) Run Program 5.1 to design a tenth order linear phase FIR bandpass filter with lower and upper cut-off frequencies at one tenth and one fifth of the sampling frequency respectively. Use a Kaiser window with $\alpha = 3$. Evaluate the frequency response by running Program 3.4, then investigate the effect of (a) reducing α to 1.5, and (b) increasing α to 5.

(5.2) Derive the impulse response $\{h[n]\}$ for an ideal digital band-stop filter with zero phase and cut-off frequencies ω_1 and ω_2. Repeat for quadrature phase. These formulae are incorporated in Program 5.1.

(5.3) An ideal bandpass digital filter with unit gain for $0 < |\omega| < \pi$ and quadrature phase is termed a 'Hilbert transformer'. Design a tenth order FIR filter which approximates this frequency response. Plot the filter's gain response (using Program 3.4), and investigate its response to sinusoidal inputs at a number of different frequencies. (Ideally all sinusoids should be delayed by a constant number of samples, in this case five, and phase shifted by 90 degrees.)

(5.4) Redesign the bandpass filter specified in Problem (5.1) using Program 5.2. Compare the frequency responses obtained.

(5.5) Write BASIC programs to implement the lowpass filter designed using Program 5.1 (see sample run) according to the alternative signal flow graphs given in Figures 5.10 and 5.11.

(5.6) The function $V_n(\Omega) = \cos(n \cos^{-1}(\Omega))$ used for the Chebychev approximation (5.28) may be written as $V_n(\Omega) = \cos(ny)$ with $y = \cos^{-1}(\Omega)$. Show that $V_0(\Omega) = 1$, $V_1(\Omega) = \Omega$ and that for $n > 1$

$$V_{n+1}(\Omega) + V_{n-1}(\Omega) = 2\Omega V_n(\Omega)$$

Hence derive expressions for $V_2(\Omega)$, $V_3(\Omega)$ and $V_4(\Omega)$. Deduce that for any integer $n > 0$, $V_n(\Omega)$ can be expressed as an nth order polynomial in Ω. Each of these polynomials is termed a 'Chebychev' polynomial.

(5.7) Use the impulse invariance technique (Program 5.7) to design a fourth order IIR bandpass filter with cut-off frequencies at one fifth and one quarter of the sampling fequency. Use a Chebychev-type analogue prototype filter with a passband ripple of 0.5 dB.

(5.8) Show that for each pole z_p of $H(z)$ obtained from $H_a(s)$ by a bilinear transformation (5.48), there must be a pole $\sigma_p + j\Omega_p$ of $H_a(s)$ such that $z_p = (1 + \sigma_p + j\Omega_p)/(1 - \sigma_p - j\Omega_p)$. Hence prove Property 1 in Section 5.11.1 by showing that if all poles of $H_a(s)$ have negative real parts σ_p, all poles of $H(z)$ will satisfy $|z_p| < 1$.

(5.9) A lowpass IIR digital filter is required with a 3 dB cut-off frequency at $\pi/2$ radians/sample and a stop-band attenuation of at least 14 dB for frequencies between $\pi/3$ and $\pi/2$. If the filter is to be designed by applying the bilinear transformation to a Butterworth-type analogue transfer function, show that the minimum order required is three. Design the filter as a serial cascade of two sections and check its frequency response using Program 3.5.

(5.10) Simulate the IIR notch filter designed in Section 3.12 in 16-bit fixed point arithmetic.

(5.11) Why is saturation overflow mode recommended for IIR filters but not for FIR filters?

(5.12) Run Program 3.5 to compare the frequency responses produced by $H(z)$ in Equation (5.63) and its integerized version in Equation (5.64). What would be the effect of using (a) 2^{15} or (b) 2^{10} instead of 2^{14} to produce Equation (5.64) from (5.63)?

(5.13) Observe the effect of a small scale limit cycle by running Program 5.10 and entering a unit impulse in Q10 format as the input sequence. What difficulties could this cause in a digital hi-fi system for example? Different cycles may be found by entering other sequences. Can you find any different cycles?

Chapter 6

Fast Fourier transform methods

6.1 Introduction

Fast Fourier transform methods were first introduced by Cooley and Tukey in 1965 (Reference 1) and are now used extensively in all areas of digital signal processing. The fast Fourier transform (FFT) is a collective term for a number of efficient algorithms developed to compute the discrete Fourier transform (DFT) and the inverse discrete Fourier transform (IDFT). It is not a transform in its own right and the understanding and interpretation of FFT methods depend fundamentally on the theory and properties of the DFT. The important properties of the DFT will therefore be discussed first in this chapter before introducing a specific FFT algorithm known as 'decimation in time'. It is not difficult to run DFT programs on a microcomputer and FFT algorithms can be quite satisfactorily demonstrated without excessive demands on memory or processing rates. A variety of BASIC programs are provided to enable most of the FFT methods discussed in this chapter to be tried and tested.

6.2 Discrete Fourier transform (DFT)

Given a finite sequence, $\{x[n]\}_{0,N-1}$, of N complex samples the DFT expression:

$$X[k] = \sum_{n=0}^{N-1} x[n]\, e^{-j2\pi nk/N} \quad k = 0, 1, \ldots, N - 1 \qquad (6.1)$$

generates a finite sequence of N frequency domain samples, $\{X[k]\}_{0,N-1}$. It has been shown in Chapter 2 (see Section 2.4) that if $X(e^{j\omega})$ is the DTFT of the windowed sequence:

$$\{\ldots, 0, 0, 0, x[0], x[1], x[2], \ldots x[N-1], 0, 0, 0, \ldots\}$$

then the values of $\{X[k]\}_{0,N-1}$ are equally spaced samples of $X(e^{j\omega})$ at intervals of $2\pi/N$ radians per sample.

If the definition of $X[k]$ in Equation (6.1) is extended to allow any value of k then $X[k]$ becomes a periodic function of k with period N since

$$X[k] = X[k + N] \qquad -\infty < k < \infty \qquad (6.2)$$

as may be seen by replacing k by $k + N$ in Equation (6.1). Equation (6.2) is consistent with the periodic nature of the DTFT discussed in Section 4.2. It follows that although the DFT specifies frequency samples of the DTFT over the range from $\omega = 0$ to 2π this information is sufficient to determine sample values for $-\infty < \omega < \infty$. For example, it is common to specify the spectrum of a discrete time signal over the frequency range from $\omega = -\pi$ to $+\pi$ and frequency samples over this range can be obtained from the DFT by setting $X[-k] = X[N-k]$ for $k = 0, 1, \ldots, (N-1)$.

Because DFT input and output sequences are always finite it will be convenient in this chapter to omit the suffix '$0, N-1$' where this does not cause ambiguity. Thus $\{x[n]\}$ and $\{X[k]\}$ will normally denote the finite sequences, $\{x[n]\}_{0,N-1}$ and $\{X[k]\}_{0,N-1}$ respectively.

6.2.1 DFT of real sequences

The DFT output sequence illustrated in Table 6.1 was obtained by running Program 2.2 with $N = 8$ and the real input sequence $\{1, 1, 1, 0, 0, 0, 0, 0\}$.

Table 6.1 A DFT output sequence ($N = 8$)

k	Real part	Imaginary part	Magnitude
0	3	0	3
1	1.7071	−1.7071	2.4142
2	0	−1	1
3	0.2929	0.2929	0.4142
4	1	0	1
5	0.2929	−0.2929	0.4142
6	0	1	1
7	1.7071	1.7071	2.4142

The spectral symmetry of the DFT of a real signal has been discussed in Section 2.4. If the values of $\{x[n]\}$ are real then $X[N-k] = X^*[k]$ and this is apparent from the example of Table 6.1 for $N = 8$. In general, it follows from this property that for real signals only:

$$|X[k]| = |X[N-k]| \qquad (6.3)$$

$$\angle X[k] = -\angle X[N-k] \qquad (6.4)$$

$$\text{Re}\, X[k] = \text{Re}\, X[N-k] \qquad (6.5)$$

$$\text{Im}\, X[k] = -\text{Im}\, X[N-k] \qquad (6.6)$$

where $\angle X[k] = \arctan(\text{Im}\, X[k]/\text{Re}\, X[k])$.

Each of these properties implies symmetry about the frequency sample at $k = N/2$ and is an important general property of the DFT of real input sequences. It also follows, by setting $k = 0$ or $k = N/2$ in Equation (6.1), that $X[0]$ and $X[N/2]$ are always real for real sequences.

6.3 Inverse discrete Fourier transform (IDFT)

The finite sequence, $\{x[n]\}$, may be expressed in terms of its frequency samples, $\{X[k]\}$, by means of the IDFT [see Section 2.4]:

$$x[n] = \frac{1}{N} \sum_{k=0}^{N-1} X[k]\, e^{j2\pi nk/N} \quad n = 0, 1, \ldots, (N-1) \qquad (6.7)$$

Similar considerations apply to the index n in the IDFT as to the index k in the DFT Equation (6.1). Normally n is specified in the range 0 to $N-1$ but by extending the range of n in Equation (6.7), $x[n]$ can be interpreted as a periodic function of n such that $x[n+N] = x[n]$ for any value of n. Apart from a single sign change and scaling by $1/N$, the IDFT expression (6.7) is identical to the DFT expression (6.1). It is therefore straightforward to modify a DFT program to evaluate the IDFT and it is usual to base both DFT and IDFT computation on the same program.

6.4 Circular and linear shifts

Two types of shift operations can be applied to finite sequences. A 'circular shift' is a rotation of the samples of a finite sequence from the last position to the first or vice versa. For example, a circular shift of the sequence $\{x[0], x[1], x[2], x[3], x[4]\}$ two places to the right results in the sequence $\{x[3], x[4], x[0], x[1], x[2]\}$. A 'linear shift' simply translates all samples to the right (or left) with zero-valued samples entering from the left (or right) as required. For example, linearly shifting the 5-sample sequence $\{x(0), x(1), x[2], x[3], x[4]\}$ two places to the right produces the sequence, $\{0, 0, x[0], x[1], x[2]\}$, losing $x[3]$ and $x[4]$. In general, a finite sequence, $\{x[n]\}$, shifted L places to the right can be un-ambiguously referred to as $\{x[n - L]\}$ provided it is clear whether a circular or linear shift is implied.

6.4.1 DFT of a circularly-shifted sequence

Let the N-sample sequence $\{x[n]\}$ be circularly shifted to produce the finite sequence:

$$\{y[n]\} = \{x[n - L]\} \tag{6.8}$$

The DFT of $\{y[n]\}$ is given by:

$$Y[k] = \sum_{n=0}^{N-1} x[n - L]\, e^{-j2\pi nk/N}$$

$$= e^{-j2\pi Lk/N} \sum_{n-0}^{N-1} x[n - L]\, e^{-j2\pi(n-L)k/N} \quad k = 0, 1, \ldots, (N-1) \tag{6.9}$$

Since, for a circular shift, $x[n] = x[n + N]$, the summation is just a reordering of the DFT summation of Equation (6.1) and:

$$Y[k] = e^{-j2\pi Lk/N} \sum_{n=0}^{N-1} x[n]\, e^{-j2\pi nk/N}$$

$$= e^{-j2\pi Lk/N} X[k] \quad k = 0, 1, \ldots, (N-1) \tag{6.10}$$

where $\{X[k]\}$ is the DFT of the unshifted sequence, $\{x[n]\}$. Because $|e^{-j2\pi Lk/N}| = 1$, circularly shifting a time sequence by L samples leaves the magnitudes of the frequency samples unaffected but modifies the phases by a term, $-2\pi Lk/N$ radians, which varies linearly with k.

6.5 Circular convolution

It has been shown (see Section 3.6) that the output of any LTI system is the discrete time convolution of the input sequence and the system's impulse response. Such a system may therefore be realized directly by implementing the discrete convolution equation (see Equation (3.19)) and this is how FIR filters are normally realized (see Figure 5.1). An alternative but potentially more efficient method uses the FFT to exploit DFT/IDFT relationships although some care is needed in interpreting the resulting convolved output because 'circular' rather than linear convolution is performed.

The circular convolution of two finite sequences of N samples, $\{x[n]\}$ and $\{h[n]\}$ is defined as:

$$y[n] = \sum_{r=0}^{N-1} h[r]x[n-r] \quad n = 0, 1, \ldots, N-1 \qquad (6.11)$$

where $x[n-r]$ is taken as a circular shift. The finite sequence, $\{y[n]\}$, can be interpreted as the output of an FIR filter with impulse response $\{h[n]\}$ and periodic input formed by repetitions of the N input samples, $\{x[n]\}$. This is illustrated in Figure 6.1 for $N=4$ where $y[0]$ is generated by summing the four products with the input samples in the position shown. Rotating the input samples then generates $y[1], y[2], y[3], y[0], y[1], \ldots$. etc. The general equation [see Equation (3.12)] for the output of an FIR filter and Equation (6.11) appears similar but the input to an FIR filter will not in general be periodic and consequently the type of convolution performed by an FIR filter is linear rather than circular.

6.5.1 DFT of a circular convolution

The DFT of the circular convolution of (6.11) is given by:

$$Y[k] = \sum_{n=0}^{N-1} \left(\sum_{r=0}^{N-1} h[r]x[n-r] \right) e^{-j2\pi nk/N} \quad k = 0, 1, \ldots, (N-1)$$

$$= \sum_{r=0}^{N-1} h[r] \sum_{n=0}^{N-1} x[n-r] e^{-j2\pi nk/N} \qquad (6.12)$$

The second summation is the DFT of $\{x[n]\}$ circularly shifted by r samples. Therefore, using the shift relationship of Equation (6.10):

$$Y[k] = \sum_{r=0}^{N-1} h[r] X[k] e^{-j2\pi nk/N}$$

$$= H[k]X[k] \quad k = 0, 1, \ldots, (N-1) \qquad (6.13)$$

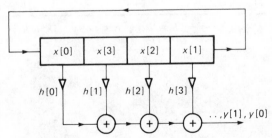

Figure 6.1 Illustration of a circular convolution ($N=4$)

where $\{H[k]\}$ is the DFT of $\{h[n]\}$. Circular convolution of two sequences is therefore equivalent to sample by sample multiplication of their individual DFTs. It follows that taking the IDFT of the product of the DFTs of two sequences results in the same type of convolution as the direct expression of Equation (6.11). It will be shown in Section 6.11 that this DFT/IDFT relationship can be used to perform linear convolution providing an alternative approach to FIR filter implementation.

6.6 The fast Fourier transform (FFT)

If the DFT is evaluated directly using Equation (6.1) then N complex multiplications must be performed for each $X[k]$ leading to a total of N^2 operations for the entire transform. The main advantage of using an FFT algorithm is a reduction in computational effort to about $N/2 \log_2 N$ complex multiplications. This makes for significant computational savings particularly for large values of N as Table 6.2 illustrates. A wide range of programs for performing various FFT algorithms are available in a variety of high-level languages (see Reference 3 for FORTRAN programs). A BASIC subroutine will be presented later in this chapter followed by several programs which demonstrate its use in signal processing applications.

Although a sound understanding of the principles and properties of the DFT is necessary to apply the FFT and interpret the output of FFT programs, in many applications an FFT subroutine can be used as a 'black box' without a detailed knowledge of the algorithm employed. Readers with a main interest in applications may therefore prefer to skip to Section 6.8 or at least defer the detailed study of an FFT algorithm which follows.

Table 6.2 Comparison of number of complex multiplications for DFT evaluation using direct (D) and FFT (F) methods

N	$D = N^2$ (Direct)	$F = N/2\log_2 N$ (FFT)	D/F
16	256	32	8
64	4096	192	21
256	65536	1024	64
1024	1.05×10^6	5120	205
4096	1.68×10^7	24576	683
16384	2.68×10^8	114688	2341
65536	4.29×10^9	524288	8192

6.6.1 *Decimation in time algorithm*

The principle on which this FFT algorithm is based involves replacing an N-sample DFT by two $N/2$-sample DFTs and then combining the outputs. If N is large this reduces the number of complex multiplications from about N^2 to $2(N/2)^2 = N^2/2$ so that computational savings of about 50% can be expected by a single application of this procedure. First, the N-sample input sequence is split into two $N/2$-sample sequences according to odd and even indices. The $N/2$-sample sequences are then split in the same way into $N/4$ sample sequences and so on until only trivial 1-sample DFTs remain. N must be a power of two to allow continued division by two.

From the DFT definition of Equation (6.1):

$$X[k] = \sum_{n=0}^{N-1} x[n]\, W^{nk} \quad k = 0, 1, \ldots, N-1 \tag{6.14}$$

where $W = e^{-j2\pi/N}$. Expanding Equation (6.14) as a sum of odd and even-indexed sequences:

$$X[k] = \sum_{n=0}^{N/2-1} x[2n]\, W^{2nk} + \sum_{n=0}^{N/2-1} x[2n+1]\, W^{(2n+1)k}$$

$$= \sum_{n=0}^{N/2-1} x[2n]\, W^{2nk} + W^k \sum_{n=0}^{N/2-1} x[2n+1]\, W^{2nk} \tag{6.15}$$

Since $W^{2n} = e^{-j2\pi n/(N/2)}$ the two sums in Equation (6.15) are recognizable as the individual DFTs of even and odd-indexed $N/2$-sample sequences. Denoting these by $E[k]$ and $F[k]$ respectively Equation (6.15) can be expressed:

$$X[k] = E[k] + W^k F[k] \tag{6.16}$$

Also, replacing k with $(k + N/2)$ in Equation (6.15) and noting that $W^{mN} = 1$ and $W^{N/2} = -1$, gives a convenient expression for computing $X[k]$ for $k \geq N/2$; that is:

$$X[k + N/2] = E[k] - W^k F[k] \tag{6.17}$$

Equations (6.16) and (6.17) specify how the DFT of the original sequence, $\{x[n]\}$, can be derived by combining the DFTs of the two $N/2$ sample sequences. The process is illustrated in Figure 6.2(a) for the generation of an 8-sample DFT from two 4-sample DFTs. The top output of each node carries the sum of its two inputs and the bottom output the difference while the arrows denote constant multipliers. Given a particular pair of values $E[k]$ and $F[k]$, $X[k]$

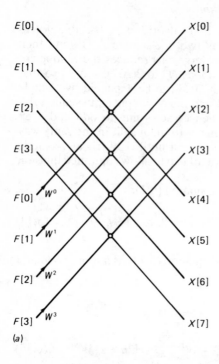

(a)

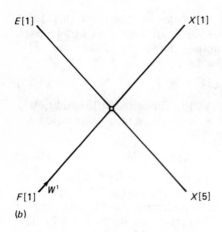

(b)

Figure 6.2 (a) Reduction of 8-sample DFT to two 4-sample DFTs (b) Single butterfly

and $X[k + N/2]$ can be most efficiently computed from Equations (6.16) and (6.17) by adding and subtracting the product $W^k F[k]$ to and from $E[k]$. For example, with $N = 8$, $X[1]$ and $X[5]$ in Figure 6.2(a) are computed by forming the sum and difference of $E[1]$ and $W^1 F[1]$ as illustrated in Figure 6.2(b). W^k is known as a 'twiddle factor' since it merely rotates $F[k]$ through an angle of $-2\pi k/N$ radians without affecting its magnitude. For a particular value of k the pair of Equations (6.16) and (6.17) is commonly known as a 'butterfly' because of the symmetry of its flowgraph evident in Figure 6.2(b). In general, only one complex multiplication is required to compute the two outputs $X[k]$ and $X[k + N/2]$ for each butterfly. A total of $N/2$ complex multiplications is therefore required to compute the complete N-sample transform from two $N/2$ sample transforms.

If N is divisible by 4, a further decomposition of the two $N/2$ sample DFTs can be performed resulting in four $N/4$ sample DFTs. For example, the inputs to the two 4-sample DFTs in Figure 6.2(a) could be derived from the outputs of the four 2-sample DFTs of $\{x[0], x[4]\}$, $\{x[2], x[6]\}$, $\{x[1], x[5]\}$ and $\{x[3], x[7]\}$. Assuming N is a power of 2, this process can be carried on for a total of $\log_2 N$ stages until only 1-sample transforms remain. This is illustrated in Figure 6.3 for $N = 8$ in which case three stages are required. Since the transform of a 1-sample sequence has the same value as the

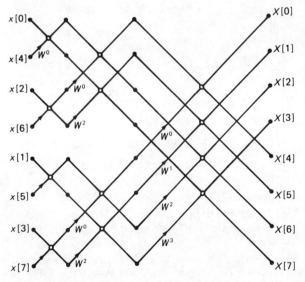

Figure 6.3 Complete reduction of 8-sample DFT

sample this is a trivial calculation. Computation is started by taking the input sequence as N, 1-sample transforms and proceeding from left to right as in Figure 6.3 computing $2, 4, 8, \ldots$ sample DFTs in successive waves of butterfly calculations until the full N-sample DFT is formed from two $N/2$ sample DFTs.

6.6.2 Bit shuffling

It can be seen from the example of Figure 6.3 for $N = 8$ that the decimation in time algorithm requires the indices of the input, $\{x[n]\}$, to be re-ordered or 'shuffled' into the order $0, 4, 2, 6, 1, 5, 3, 7$ to arrive at a natural output ordering. This re-ordering can be achieved by reversing the digits of the indices expressed as binary numbers. Bit reversal is illustrated in Table 6.3 for $N = 8$. Because the input sequence will usually be given in a natural ordering, bit shuffling must be performed in a preliminary stage before this FFT algorithm is applied. (A different algorithm named 'decimation in frequency' (Reference 4) shuffles output rather than input samples to achieve the same result.)

Table 6.3 Bit reversal ($N = 8$)

Decimal	Binary	Reversed binary	Decimal
0	000	000	0
1	001	100	4
2	010	010	2
3	011	110	6
4	100	001	1
5	101	101	5
6	110	011	3
7	111	111	7

6.6.3 Summary of procedure for decimation in time algorithm

Assuming N is a power of 2 the decimation in time algorithm requires the following steps:

(1) Bit reverse input sequence,
(2) Compute $N/2$, 2-sample DFTs from the shuffled input,
(3) Compute $N/4$, 4-sample DFTs from the 2-sample DFTs generated by step 2,
(4) Continue to compute $N/8$, 8-sample DFTs, $N/16$, 16-sample DFTs etc. in successive stages until one N-sample DFT is computed from 2, $N/2$ sample DFTs.

6.7 Computational aspects of the FFT

A very important property of any FFT algorithm is that computation can be done 'in place' resulting in efficient use of memory. That is, the same memory locations can be used to store the input sequence, the results of intermediate DFTs and the final output sequence. This is possible because each pair of samples in a butterfly calculation is required only once in a particular stage. The two results of a butterfly can therefore be allowed to overwrite the values used in their calculation so that the N values stored in the input sequence memory locations are completely replaced after every stage.

The need to access the various twiddle factors will also affect memory considerations. If speed is crucial then twiddle factors can be precomputed and stored in a look-up table for rapid access; this is done in Program 6.1 which follows. Otherwise, sine and cosine values can be computed as they are needed although this can be timeconsuming. The speed advantage of the FFT derives primarily from the breakdown of computational effort into $\log_2 N$ stages and, since $N/2$ butterflies require $N/2$ complex multiplications at each stage, a total of $\frac{1}{2}N\log_2 N$ are required for the complete DFT. This compares with N^2 for the direct method and confers the computational advantage illustrated in Table 6.2.

Program 6.1 introduces a general-purpose FFT subroutine using the decimation in time algorithm for complex input sequences. A real input consisting of an 8-sample sinusoidal sequence is used for sample run 1. The relative frequency is set at $\pi/2$ (or $1/4T$ Hz) corresponding to exactly 2 periods over eight samples and resulting in non-zero frequency samples only for $X[2]$ and $X[6]$. This can be verified by direct calculation from Equation (6.1). Since the input is real, $X[6] = X^*[8 - 6] = X^*[2]$ (Section 6.2.1). This property is also evident for any value of k in sample run 2 for $N = 16$ for which the input is a unit pulse consisting of four unit samples. In this case the output, $X[0] = 4$ is easily verified since $X[0]$ is always the sum of input sample values. Also, $X[0]$ and $X[8]$ are both real as shown in Section 6.2.1.

Program 6.1 can be used to verify any of the DFT properties discussed in earlier sections. For example, in sample run 3, the unit pulse of sample run 2 is circularly shifted by $N/2 = 8$ samples in which case Equation (6.10) predicts that the corresponding DFT should be multiplied by $e^{-j2\pi 8k/16} = (-1)^k$. This is verified by comparing the outputs of sample runs 2 and 3.

Program 6.1 FFT: DFT evaluation using FFT decimation in time algorithm

```
10 REM FFT
20 DEF FNA(X)=INT(10000*X+0.5)/10000
30 PRINT "TYPE X WHERE NO. OF SAMPLES = 2^X";
40 INPUT M
50 NS=2^M
60 DIM XR(NS),XI(NS),SI(NS),CO(NS),X(NS)
70 PRINT "DEFINE REAL PART OF INPUT"
80 GOSUB 10000 : REM ARRAY DEFN. SUB.
90 FOR N=0 TO NS-1 : XR(N)=X(N) : NEXT N
100 PRINT "DEFINE IMAG. PART OF INPUT"
110 GOSUB 10000 : REM ARRAY DEFN. SUB.
120 FOR N=0 TO NS-1 : XI(N)=X(N) : NEXT N
130 PRINT"FORWARD(1) OR INVERSE(-1) TRANSFORM";
140 INPUT IN
145 GOSUB 30000 : REM FFT SUB.
150 PRINT " K         REAL        IMAG        MAG"
160 FOR K=0 TO NS-1
170 PRINT K,FNA(XR(K)),FNA(XI(K)),
180 PRIKT FNA(SQR(XR(K)*XR(K)+XI(K)*XI(K)))
190 NEXT K
200 END
10000 REM - - ARRAY DEFINITION SUB. - -
[- - etc. see Program 1.4 - -]


30000 REM - - FFT SUBROUTINE - -
30010 REM - COMPUTE TWIDDLE FACTORS -
30020 KK=6.28318/NS : REM 2PI/NS
30030 FOR N=0 TO NS-1
30040 K1=N*KK
30050 CO(N)=COS(K1) : SI(N)=-SIN(K1)*IN
30060 NEXT N
30080 REM - - BIT REVERSAL - -
30090 NS=2^M : N2=NS/2 : NM=NS-1 : J0=0
30100 FOR I0=0 TO NM-1
30110 IF I0>J0 THEN 30150
30120 CR=XR(J0) : CI=XI(J0)
30130 XR(J0)=XR(I0) : XI(J0)=XI(I0)
30140 XR(I0)=CR : XI(I0)=CI
30150 K=N2
30160 IF K>=J0+1 THEN 30180
30170 J0=J0-K : K=K/2 : GOTO 30160
30180 J0=J0+K
30190 NEXT I0
30195 REM --- FFT ALOGORITHM ---
30200 FOR L=1 TO M
30210 LE=2^L : L1=LE/2 : UR=1 : UI=0 : JJ=0
30220 IK=NS/LE
30230 FOR J=0 TO L-1
30240 FOR I=J TO NS-1 STEP LE
30250 IP=I+L1
30260 CR=XR(IP)*UR-XI(IP)*UI
30270 CI=XI(IP)*UR+XR(IP)*UI
30280 XR(IP)=XR(I)-CR : XI(IP)=XI(I)-CI
30290 XR(I)=XR(I)+CR : XI(I)=XI(I)+CI
```

```
30300 NEXT I
30310 JJ=JJ+IK
30320 UR=CO(JJ) : UI=SI(JJ)
30330 NEXT J
30340 NEXT L
30350 IF IN>0 THEN RETURN
30360 REM - - DO IF IDFT - -
30370 FOR N=0 TO NS-1
30380 XR(N)=XR(N)/NS : XI(N)=XI(N)/NS
30390 NEXT N
30400 RETURN
```

Sample run 1

```
TYPE X WHERE NO. OF SAMPLES = 2^X ? 3
DEFINE REAL PART OF INPUT
SEQUENCE TYPE? SN
PERIODS OVER 8 SAMPLES? 2
NO. SAMPLES DELAY? 0
DEFINE IMAG. PART OF INPUT
SEQUENCE TYPE? ZE
FORWARD(1) OR INVERSE(-1) TRANSFORM ? 1
```

K	REAL	IMAG	MAG
0	.0000	.00000	.0000
1	.0000	.00000	.0000
2	.0000	-4.00000	4.0000
3	.0000	.00000	.0000
4	.0000	.00000	.0000
5	.0000	.00000	.0000
6	.0000	4.00000	4.0000
7	.0000	.00000	.0000

Sample run 2

```
TYPE X WHERE NO. OF SAMPLES = 2^X ? 4
DEFINE REAL PART OF INPUT
SEQUENCE TYPE? UP
STARTING/ENDING SAMPLE NOS. ? 12,15
DEFINE IMAG. PART OF INPUT
SEQUENCE TYPE? ZE
FORWARD(1) OR INVERSE(-1) TRANSFORM ? 1
```

K	REAL	IMAG	MAG
0	4.0000	.0000	4.0000
1	2.0137	3.0137	3.6245
2	-1.0000	2.4142	2.6131
3	-1.2483	.2483	1.2728
4	.0000	.0000	.0000
5	-.1659	.8341	.8504
6	-1.0000	.4142	1.0824
7	-.5995	-.4005	.7210
8	.0000	.0000	.0000
9	-.5995	.4005	.7210
10	-1.0000	-.4142	1.0824
11	-.1659	-.8341	.8504
12	.0000	.0000	.0000
13	-1.2483	-.2483	1.2728
14	-1.0000	-2.4142	2.6131
15	2.0137	-3.0137	3.6245

148   *Fast Fourier transform methods*

Sample run 3

TYPE X WHERE NO. OF SAMPLES = 2^X ? 4
DEFINE REAL PART OF INPUT
SEQUENCE TYPE? UP
STARTING/ENDING SAMPLE NUMBERS ? 4,7
DEFINE IMAG. PART OF INPUT
SEQUENCE TYPE? ZE
FORWARD(1) OR INVERSE(-1) TRANSFORM ? 1
 K   REAL   IMAG   MAG
 0   4.0000   .0000   4.0000
 1   -2.0137   -3.0137   3.6245
 2   -1.0000   2.4142   2.6131
 3   1.2483   -.2483   1.2728
 4   .0000   .0000   .0000
 5   .1659   -.8341   .8504
 6   -1.0000   .4142   1.0824
 7   .5995   .4005   .7210
 8   .0000   .0000   .0000
 9   .5995   -.4005   .7210
10   -1.0000   -.4142   1.0824
11   .1659   .8341   .8504
12   .0000   .0000   .0000
13   1.2483   .2483   1.2728
14   -1.0000   -2.4142   2.6131
15   -2.0137   3.0137   3.6245
```

*Program notes*

(1) The array definition subroutine 10000 is called twice to place real and imaginary parts of the input sequence in arrays XR and XI. Due to the 'in place' property of the FFT calculation the output is returned in the same arrays. Real and imaginary parts and magnitudes of the output are printed after rounding using function FNA defined in statement 20.

(2) The FFT subroutine 30000 precalculates NS sine and cosine values for the twiddle factors in arrays SI and CO. (If it is known that twiddle factors have already been calculated for a particular value of NS then repetition of the precalculation can be avoided by calling the subroutine from statement 30080.)

(3) Either forward or inverse transforms can be calculated depending on whether IN is 1 or −1 respectively on input to the FFT subroutine. The variable IN is used within the subroutine to effectively change the sign of the exponent for DFT or IDFT and divide the output by N in the case of the IDFT.

### 6.8 Applications of the FFT

FFT algorithms can be used to great advantage in a wide range of signal processing applications. These include Fourier analysis and
```

synthesis of signals and spectrum analysis in general but it will also be seen that FFT methods can be used to implement FIR digital filters. The remaining sections of this chapter are devoted to a number of common FFT applications which will be discussed and exemplified using the FFT subroutine in Program 6.1.

6.9 Fourier analysis and synthesis using the FFT

If $\{x[n]\}$ is a real periodic sequence of period N samples then the IDFT expression (6.7) can be manipulated to express $\{x[n]\}$ as a Fourier series in terms of sampled sine and cosine harmonic components (see Section 2.2.1). From expression (6.7):

$$x[n] = \frac{1}{N} \sum_{k=0}^{N-1} X[k] e^{j2\pi nk/N} \quad n = 0, 1, \ldots, (N-1) \quad (6.18)$$

Removing the terms $X[0]$ and $X[N/2]$ from the summation and setting $W = e^{j\pi/N}$:

$$x[n] = \frac{1}{N} \sum_{k=1}^{N/2-1} (X[k] W^{nk} + X[N-k] W^{n[N-k]})$$

$$+ \frac{X[0]}{N} + \frac{X[N/2] e^{j\pi n}}{N} \quad (6.19)$$

Now $e^{j\pi n} = (-1)^n$, $W^{n(N-k)} = W^{-nk} = (W^{nk})^*$ and, as shown in Section 6.2.1, if $\{x[n]\}$ is real, $X[k] = X^*[N-k]$ where $*$ denotes complex conjugation. Therefore:

$$x[n] = \frac{1}{N} \left[\sum_{k=1}^{N/2-1} 2 \operatorname{Re}(X[k] W^{nk}) \right]$$

$$+ \frac{X[0]}{N} + \frac{X[N/2](-1)^n}{N} \quad (6.20)$$

where Re denotes 'real part of'. Now if W^{nk} is expanded as $\cos(2\pi nk/N) + j \sin(2\pi nk/N)$ and $X[k]$ as $\operatorname{Re}(X[k]) + j \operatorname{Im}(X[k])$ where Im denotes 'imaginary part of', then:

$$x[n] = \frac{1}{N} \left[\sum_{k-1}^{N/2-1} 2\{\operatorname{Re}(X[k]) \cos(2\pi nk/N) \right.$$

$$\left. - \operatorname{Im}(X[k]) \sin(2\pi nk/N)\} \right]$$

$$+ \frac{X[0]}{N} + \frac{X[N/2]}{N} \cos(\pi n) \quad (6.21)$$

This is now a conventional sine/cosine Fourier series of the form:

$$x[n] = \sum_{k=0}^{N/2} a_k \cos(2\pi nk/N) + \sum_{k=1}^{N/2-1} b_k \sin(2\pi nk/N) \qquad (6.22)$$

where the real constants $\{a_k\}$ and $\{b_k\}$ are Fourier series coefficients. Comparing Equation (6.21) with (6.22) the coefficients are given by:

$$a_k = \frac{2}{N} \operatorname{Re}(X[k]),$$

$$b_k = \frac{-2}{N} \operatorname{Im}(X[k]) \quad k = 1, 2, \dots, (N/2 - 1)$$

$$a_0 = \frac{X[0]}{N}, \quad a_{N/2} = \frac{X[N/2]}{N} \qquad (6.23)$$

6.9.1 Fourier analysis of a sequence

The transformations (6.23), from DFT coefficients to Fourier series coefficients, can be readily incorporated in a DFT program such as Program 6.1 to generate a set of Fourier series coefficients given one period of N samples of a periodic sequence. If the input samples are obtained by sampling an analogue signal then the analogue signal should be bandlimited to less than half the sampling frequency as dictated by the sampling theorem otherwise aliasing will distort the spectrum (see Section 4.4.1). This digital method of Fourier analysis can therefore only be applied to periodic analogue signals which are effectively bandlimited and therefore known to be characterised by no more than N Fourier series coefficients.

6.9.2 Signal synthesis using FFT

If the relationships of Equations (6.23) are inverted so that, $\{X[k]\}$, is derived from a given set of Fourier series coefficients then the IDFT can be used to synthesize a period of the time sequence, $\{x[n]\}$. Program 6.2 uses FFT subroutine 30000 to synthesize a real sequence according to Equation (6.22) from a specification of the phase and magnitude of each harmonic term. In the sample run, the coefficients specified correspond to the first three non-zero harmonics of a 32 sample 'square' wave. Elimination of the remaining harmonics is a lowpass filtering operation and the effect of this on the time sequence is readily apparent in the output which is plotted in Figure 6.4.

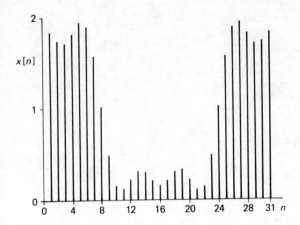

Figure 6.4 Synthesis of square wave from three harmonics

Program 6.2 SIGSYN: signal synthesis

```
5 REM SIGSYN
10 PRINT "TYPE X WHERE NO. OF SAMPLES = 2^X";
20 DEF FNA(X)=INT (X*10000+0.5)/10000
30 INPUT M : NS=2^M
40 DIM XR(NS+2),XI(NS),CO(NS),SI(NS)
50 PRINT "CONSTANT COMPONENT A(0)";
60 N2=NS/2 : P1=4*ATN(1)
70 INPUT A0
80 XR(0)=A0*NS : XI(0)=0
90 REM - - INPUT FOURIER COEFFS. - -
100 PRINT "MAG., PHASE(DEGREES)"
110 FOR K=1 TO N2-1
120 PRINT "COEFFICIENT NO.";K;
130 INPUT MG,PH : PH=PH*P1/180
140 IF MG<0 THEN 180
150 XR(K)=N2*MG*COS(PH) : XI(K)=-N2*MG*SIN(PH)
160 NEXT K
170 REM - - FILL XI & XR FOR FFT - -
180 PRINT "COS COEFF"; -N2;
190 INPUT CC
200 XR(N2)=NS*CC : XI(N2)=0
210 FOR K=1 TO N2-1
220 XR(NS-K)=XR(K) : XI(NS-K)=-XI(K)
230 NEXT K
240 IN=-1
250 REM - - CALL FFT & PRINTOUT - -
260 GOSUB 30000 : REM FFT SUB.
270 PRINT "OUTPUT  : -"
280 FOR N=0 TO NS-1
290 PRINT FNA(XR(N));
300 NEXT N
310 END
```

```
30000 REM - - FFT SUB. - -
[- - etc. see Program 6.1 - -]

Sample run

TYPE X WHERE NO. OF SAMPLES = 2^X ? 5
CONSTANT COMPONENT A(0)? 1
MAG., PHASE(DEGREES)?
COEFFICIENT NO. 1 ?  1,0
COEFFICIENT NO. 2 ?  0,0
COEFFICIENT NO. 3 ?  .33333,180
COEFFICIENT NO. 4 ?  0,0
COEFFICIENT NO. 5 ?  .2,0
COEFFICIENT NO. 6 ? -1,0
COS COEFFICIENT NO. 16 ? 0
OUTPUT :-
 1.8667  1.8147  1.7198  1.7003  1.8014  1.9215
 1.8754  1.5466  1  .4534  .1246  .0785
 .1986  .2997  .2802  .1853  .1333  .1853
 .2802  .2997  .1986  .0785  .1246  .4534
 1  1.5466  1.8754  1.9215  1.8014  1.7003
 1.7198  1.8147
```

Program notes

(1) The program requests a value of M where $N = 2^M$ followed by definition of up to $N/2$ Fourier series coefficients. All coefficients are defined by specifying magnitude and phase values except a_0 and $a_{N/2}$ which must be real. The series can be truncated at any point by entering a negative value for a magnitude in which case all remaining coefficients with index less than $N/2$ are set to zero.

(2) The output is rounded to 4 decimal digits and printed for the sample run as a time sequence but a graphics routine should be used if possible so that the output signal can be viewed in graphical form such as in Figure 6.4.

6.10 Faster FFT for real input

If the FFT input is a real sequence as is often the case, the N memory cells corresponding to the imaginary part of input samples must be set to zero if a complex input DFT program such as Program 6.1 is used. Also, for a real sequence:

$$X[N - k] = X^*[k] \qquad (6.24)$$

as discussed in Section 6.2.1. A real sequence is therefore wholly specified by $N/2$ rather than N sample values both in time and frequency domains. These properties can be exploited to obtain computational savings by calculating the DFT of two real N-sample sequences from a single complex N-sample DFT.

Suppose $\{x[n]\}$ and $\{y[n]\}$ are two real finite sequences of N samples. Let a new complex sequence be defined as:

$$\{z[n]\} = \{x[n] + \mathrm{j}y[n]\} \quad n = 0, 1, \ldots, (N-1) \qquad (6.25)$$

Forming the DFT of $\{z[n]\}$ it follows that:

$$Z[k] = X[k] + \mathrm{j}Y[k] \quad k = 0, 1, \ldots, (N-1) \qquad (6.26)$$

Since $\{x[n]\}$ and $\{y[n]\}$ are real their DFTs must satisfy the symmetry condition of Equation (6.24). That is:

$$X[N-k] = X^*[k] \text{ and } Y[N-k] = Y^*[k] \qquad (6.27)$$

Now from Equation (6.26):

$$\begin{aligned} Z[N-k] &= X[N-k] + \mathrm{j}Y[N-k] \\ &= X^*[k] + \mathrm{j}^*Y[k] \end{aligned} \qquad (6.28)$$

and by complex conjugation:

$$Z^*[N-k] = X[k] - \mathrm{j}Y[k] \qquad (6.29)$$

Combining Equations (6.26) and (6.29):

$$X[k] = \frac{1}{2}(Z[k] + Z^*[N-k]) \qquad (6.30)$$

$$Y[k] = \frac{1}{2\mathrm{j}}(Z[k] - Z^*[N-k]) \qquad (6.31)$$

The DFT sequences $\{X[k]\}$ and $\{Y[k]\}$ can therefore be separated by forming the sums and differences of $\{Z[k]\}$ as above. About double the number of complex multiplications are required for the alternative approach of computing two separate N-sample DFTs. The method is illustrated by Program 6.3 which uses a single FFT subroutine call for simultaneous evaluation of the DFT of two real sequences.

Program 6.3 REALFFT: simultaneous FFT of two real sequences

```
10 REM REALFFT
20 PRINT "TYPE X WHERE NO. OF SAMPLES - 2^X";
30 INPUT M : NS=2^M : N2-NS/2
40 DIM X(NS),XR(NS),XI(NS),PR(N2)
50 DIM PI(N2),QR(N2),QI(N2),SI(NS),CO(NS)
60 DEF FNA(X)-INT(10000*X+0.5)/10000
70 PRINT "DEFINE 1ST REAL SIG"
80 GOSUB 10000 : REM ARRAY DEFN. SUB.
90 FOR N-0 TO NS-1 : XR(N)-X(N) : NEXT N
100 PRINT "DEFINE 2ND REAL SIG"
110 GOSUB 10000 : REM ARRAY DEFN. SUB
```

```
120 FOR N=0 TO NS-1 : XI(N)=X(N) : NEXT N
130 IN=1
140 GOSUB 30000 : REM FFT SUB.
150 XR(NS)=XR(0) : XI(NS)=XI(0)
160 FOR K=0 TO N2
170 NN=NS-K
180 PR(K)=(XR(K)+XR(NN))/2
190 PI(K)=(XI(K)-XI(NN))/2
200 QR(K)=(XI(K)+XI(NN))/2
210 QI(K)=(XR(NN)-XR(K))/2 : NEXT K
220 PRINT "DFT OF 1ST SEQUENCE (REAL, IMAGINARY)"
230 FOR K=0 TO N2 : PRINT FNA(PR(K));", ";FNA(PI(K) : NEXT K
240 PRINT "DFT OF 2ND SEQUENCE (REAL, IMAGINARY)"
250 FOR K=0 TO N2 : PRINT FNA(QR(K)); ", ";FNA(QI(K)) : NEXT K
260 END
10000 REM - - ARRAY DEFINITION SUB. - -
[- - etc. see Program 1.4 - -]

30000 REM - - FFT SUB. - -
[- - etc. see Program 6.1 - -]

Sample run

TYPE X WHERE NO. OF SAMPLES = 2^X ? 3
DEFINE 1ST REAL SIG
SEQUENCE TYPE? SN
PERIODS OVER 8 SAMPLES? 1
NO. SAMPLES DELAY? 0
DEFINE 2ND REAL SIG
SEQUENCE TYPE? IP
DFT OF 1ST SEQUENCE (REAL, IMAGINARY)
 0 , 0
 0 ,-4
 0 , 0
 0 , 0
 0 , 0
DFT OF 2ND SEQUENCE (REAL, IMAGINARY)
 1 , 0
 1 , 0
 1 , 0
 1 , 0
 1 , 0
```

Program notes

(1) Two real time sequences of NS samples each are defined by two calls to the array definition subroutine 10000 and placed in arrays XR and XI respectively. The FFT subroutine 30000 is called and Equations (6.30) and (6.31) used to form the individual transforms in arrays PR, PI and QR, QI. The program prints out real and imaginary parts of each frequency sample for both transforms only up to sample NS/2 since both DFTs are of real sequences.

(2) The sample run illustrates simultaneous DFT evaluation for

two inputs consisting of sinusoidal and impulse sequences respectively.

6.11 Fast convolution

It has been shown in Section 6.5.1 that the circular convolution of two sequences can be obtained by taking the IDFT of the sample-by-sample product of their DFTs. It will now be shown that linear convolution can be performed as a circular convolution making possible a DFT/IDFT approach to FIR linear filtering in which one of the sequences to be convolved can be a finite duration impulse response and the other a lengthy input sequence. This provides a radically different approach to FIR filtering based on 'fast' convolution using efficient FFT methods as opposed to the transversal filter realization illustrated in Figure 5.1.

6.11.1 Linear from circular convolution

If $\{x[n]\}$ and $\{h[n]\}$ are two finite sequences of N samples the discrete linear convolution of the two sequences (see Equation (3.19) in Section 3.6) is given by:

$$y[n] = \sum_{r=0}^{N-1} h[r]\,x[n-r] \qquad (6.32)$$

where $x[n-r]$ is a linear shift and therefore zero-valued samples are assumed outside the range $0 \leqslant (n-r) \leqslant N-1$. Since $x[n]$ can have nonzero values only within this range, and $0 \leqslant r \leqslant N-1$, it follows that $y[n]$ will have no more than $(N-1)$ nonzero values in the range $0 \leqslant n \leqslant 2(N-1)$. If, for example, $N=4$ then 7 nonzero values of $y[n]$ are generated for $n = 0, 1, \ldots, 6$ and are given by Equation (6.32) as:

$$y[0] = h[0]x[0]$$

$$y[1] = h[0]x[1] + h[1]x[0]$$

$$y[2] = h[0]x[2] + h[1]x[1] + h[2]x[0]$$

$$y[3] = h[0]x[3] + h[1]x[2] + h[2]x[1] + h[3]x[0]$$

$$y[4] = h[1]x[3] + h[2]x[2] + h[3]x[1]$$

$$y[5] = h[2]x[3] + h[3]x[2]$$

$$y[6] = h[3]x[3] \qquad (6.33)$$

However, exactly the same values of $y[n]$ can be generated by circular convolution provided the length of $\{x(n)\}$ is extended by

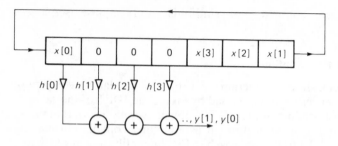

Figure 6.5 Linear via circular convolution ($N = 4$)

adding at least three zerovalued samples. This is illustrated in Figure 6.5 which should be compared with Figure 6.1. In general, the result of a linear convolution will not be the same as circular convolution but if the lengths of one or both of the sequences is increased by 'zero padding', i.e. adding zerovalued samples to the sequences, then unwanted convolution products are removed and the result of the two types of convolution can be made identical.

The following procedure will obtain the linear convolution of two N-sample sequences using the DFT/IDFT with an FFT algorithm and N a power of 2.

(1) Add N zeros to both input sequences to form $\{x[n]\}_{0,2N-1}$ and $\{h[n]\}_{0,2N-1}$. This results in two double-length sequences with $2N$ a power of 2 and sufficient zero padding to ensure that linear convolution is performed.
(2) Take the DFT of each sequence to form $\{X[k]\}_{0,2N-1}$ and $\{H[k]\}_{0,2N-1}$. This forms the individual DFTs of the double-length sequences.
(3) Multiply the DFTs, sample by sample to form, $Y[k] = H[k]X[k]$. This gives $\{Y[k]\}_{0,2N-1}$, the DFT of the convolved sequence.
(4) Take the IDFT of $\{Y[k]\}_{0,2N-1}$ to form the required output sequence $\{y[n]\}_{0,2N-1}$.

Comparing this apparently complicated procedure with direct evaluation of the convolution expression of Equation (6.32) raises questions about the term 'fast' convolution. However, both the DFTs in step 2 and the IDFT in step 4 above can be performed using an FFT algorithm and, if N is made large enough, this approach will always be faster than the direct method. Moreover, if the two sequences to be convolved are real they can be very conveniently transformed using a single DFT as discussed in Section 6.10. This requires a total of $2N \log_2 (2N)$ complex multiplications for the DFTs and the IDFT. Also, since $X[N-k] = X^*[k]$ for a real sequence (see Section (6.2.1)), only N, rather than $2N$ complex multiplications, are required to form the DFT products giving a final total of $N(3 + 2 \log_2 N)$.

Program 6.4 uses FFT subroutine 30000 to compute the convolution of two real sequences by the DFT/IDFT method. As the program does not perform zero padding it can be used for either circular or linear convolution depending on whether the user adds extra zeros or not. For example, to obtain the linear convolution of two N-sample sequences, $2N$ sample values should be input leaving N consecutive zerovalued samples at the end of each sequence. This is illustrated for linear convolution of two 'pulses' in sample run 1.

It is straightforward to check the result of a linear convolution by using Program 6.4 with simple input and impulse response sequences. For example, if:

$$\{h[n]\} = \{1, -1, 0, \ldots 0\} \tag{6.34}$$

then the output of the equivalent FIR filter [see Section 3.5] is:

$$y[n] = x[n] - x[n-1] \tag{6.35}$$

and output samples are given by the differences between successive input values. This is verified in sample run 2. Note that 'fast' convolution of such short sequences should be regarded as illustrative only as the FFT approach has a clear computational advantage only for much longer sequences.

Program 6.4 FASTCONV: fast convolution

```
10 REM FASTCONV
20 PRINT "TYPE X WHERE NO. OF SAMPLES = 2^X";
30 INPUT M : NS=2^M : N2=NS/2
40 DIM X(NS),XR(2*NS),XI(2*NS),PR(N2),PI(N2)
50 DIM QR(NS),QI(NS),SI(NS),CO(NS)
60 DEF FNA(X)=INT(X*1000+0.5)/1000
70 PRINT : PRINT"DEFINE 1ST REAL SIG"
80 GOSUB 10000 : REM ARRAY DEFN. SUB.
90 FOR N=0 TO NS-1 : XR(N)=X(N) : NEXT N
100 PRINT "DEFINE 2ND REAL SIG"
110 GOSUB 10000 : REM ARRAY DEFN. SUB.
120 FOR N=0 TO NS-1 : XI(N)=X(N) : NEXT N
130 IN=1
140 GOSUB 30000 : REM FFT SUB.
150 XR(NS)=XR(0) : XI(NS)=XI(0)
160 FOR K=0 TO N2
170 NN=NS-K
180 PR(K)=(XR(K)+XR(NN))/2
190 PI(K)=(XI(K)-XI(NN))/2
200 QR(K)=(XI(K)+XI(NN))/2
```

```
210 QI(K)=(XR(NN)-XR(K))/2 : NEXT K
220 FOR K=0 TO N2
230 R1=PR(K) : R2=QR(K) : I1=PI(K) : I2=QI(K)
240 XR(K)=R1*R2-I1*I2 : XI(K)=R1*I2+R2*I1
250 XR(NS-K)=XR(K) : XI(NS-K)=-XI(K)
260 NEXT K
270 FOR N=0 TO NS-1
280 IN=-1 : ZZ=0 : GOSUB 30000 : REM FFT SUB.
290 PRINT"CONVOLVED OUTPUT :-"
300 FOR N=0 TO NS-1
310 PRINT FNA(XR(N)); : NEXT N
320 END
10000 REM - - ARRAY DEFINITION SUB. - -
[- - etc. see Program 1.4 - -]

30000 REM - - FFT SUB. - -
[- - etc. see Program 6.1 - -]
```

Sample run 1

```
TYPE X WHERE NO. OF SAMPLES = 2^X ? 4
DEFINE 1ST REAL SIG
SEQUENCE TYPE? UP
STARTING/ENDING SAMPLE NOS. ? 0,4
DEFINE 2ND REAL SIG
SEQUENCE TYPE? UP
STARTING/ENDING SAMPLE NOS. ? 0,6
CONVOLVED OUTPUT :-
 1 2 3 4 5 5 5 4
 3 2 1 0 0 0 0 0
```

Sample run 2

```
TYPE X WHERE NO. OF SAMPLES = 2^X ? 4
DEFINE 1ST REAL SIG
SEQUENCE TYPE? ME
STARTING/ENDING AT SAMPLE NOS.? 0,1
VALUE NUMBER 0 ? 1
VALUE NUMBER 1 ?-1
DEFINE 2ND REAL SIG
SEQUENCE TYPE? ME
STARTING/ENDING AT SAMPLES NOS.? 1,5
VALUE NUMBER 1 ? 1
VALUE NUMBER 2 ? 3
VALUE NUMBER 3 ? 7
VALUE NUMBER 4 ?-7
VALUE NUMBER 5 ?-4
CONVOLVED OUTPUT :-
 0 1 2 4 -14 3 4 0
 0 0 0 0 0 0 0
```

Program notes

Two calls to the array definition subroutine 10000 define NS samples of two real input signals. The DFT of the two real sequences is computed as in Program 6.3 followed by IDFT of the product of the two DFTs. Finally, the convolved output is rounded and printed.

6.11.2 *Fast convolution FIR filters*

In general, the two sequences to be convolved will not be of the same length. For example, a filtering operation will usually require linear convolution of a finite impulse response with a considerably longer input sequence. If the impulse response and input sequences are I and N samples long respectively, then by generalizing the argument of Section 6.11.1 it can be shown that linear convolution will generate $(I + N - 1)$ significant output samples. Transform lengths of $(I + N - 1 + P)$ samples can then be used where P is any additional number of zerovalued samples necessary to make $(I + N - 1 + P)$ a power of two for FFT computation.

If the input sequence is very large in comparison with the length I of the impluse response then, to avoid problems of data storage and signal delay, it becomes necessary to split the input sequence into a number of consecutive blocks of N samples which can be convolved individually. This is an obvious requirement for real-time operation where, for all practical purposes, the input is an endless sequence. A suitable value of N is chosen to allow efficient FFT computation of $(I + N - 1)$ sample DFTs where each FFT input comprises a block of N input samples followed by $(I - 1)$ zerovalued samples. Because this generates $(I + N - 1)$ linearly convolved output sample values for every input block of N samples, outputs 'overlap' the beginning of the next output block by a 'tail' of $I - 1$ samples. The tail must therefore be added to the first $I - 1$ output samples corresponding to the next fast convolution. This process, known as the 'overlap add' method (Reference 4), is illustrated in Figure 6.6.

If inputs are real then, with $(I + N - 1)$ a power of 2, the number of complex multiplications required for each fast convolution will be:

$$\frac{(I + N - 1)}{2} [1 + 2\log_2(I + N - 1)] \tag{6.36}$$

This generates N output samples and can be compared with the NI complex multiplications required to generate the same number of output samples using direct FIR implementation (see Section 5.1). Another procedure called the 'overlap save' method (Reference 4) can be used to achieve the same result as overlap add. This is very similar but input rather than output blocks are overlapped to achieve the final convolved output.

160   *Fast Fourier transform methods*

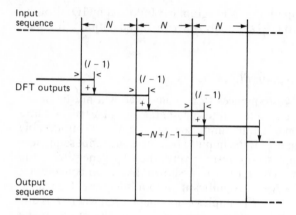

Figure 6.6 Linear convolution by overlap-add method

6.12 Decimation and interpolation

In many applications it is useful to transform a sequence representing an analogue signal sampled at a given rate to another sequence representing the same analogue signal sampled at a different rate. For example, although an analogue speech signal bandlimited to less than 5 kHz and sampled at 20 kHz is 'oversampled' in comparison with the sequence which results from sampling the same speech signal at the minimum sampling rate of 10 kHz, the additional 'interpolated' samples may well be useful for display or plotting purposes. In principle, the 20 kHz sampled sequence could be derived from the 10 kHz sequence by converting the latter back to an analogue signal and resampling at 20 kHz. This is unnecessary, however, as sampling rate transformations can be achieved directly by digital means by exploiting DFT/IDFT relationships and using the FFT for efficient computation.

Let $x_a(t)$ be an analogue signal with samples, $x[n] = x_a(nT)$. If a new sequence is required such that $y[n] = x_a(nIT)$ where I is a constant, then if $I < 1$, the sampling rate is effectively increased and the conversion process is called interpolation. If $I > 1$, the sampling rate is reduced and, since samples are lost, the process is called decimation.

6.12.1 Interpolation

Suppose the analogue signal, $x_a(t)$, is bandlimited to less than $1/2T$ Hz as illustrated in Figure 6.7(a). In accordance with the

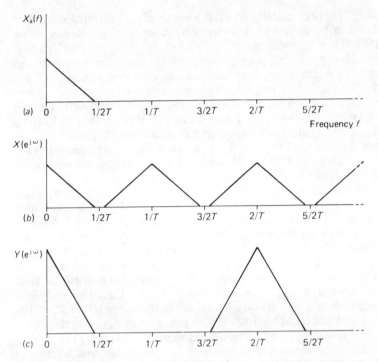

Figure 6.7 Spectra illustrating decimation and interpolation (a) analogue signal spectrum, (b) T-second sampled spectrum, $T/2$-second sampled spectrum

sampling theorem (see Section 4.2), no aliasing can occur if $1/T$ samples per second are taken. In this case, $x[n] = x_a(nT)$, and $X(e^{j\omega})$ will exhibit the usual infinite repetitions with period $1/T$ Hz as illustrated in Figure 6.7(b). Now suppose $x_a(t)$ is sampled at a rate of $2/T$ samples per second forming another sequence such that $y[n] = x_a(nT/2)$. This corresponds to interpolation with $I = 0.5$ and, $Y(e^{j\omega})$, the spectrum of $\{y[n]\}$, will repeat every $2/T$ Hz as illustrated in Figure 6.7(c). Because $x_a(t)$ is bandlimited to less than $1/2T$ Hz nonzero spectral components will be absent in the region from $1/2T$ to $3/2T$ Hz and each spectral repetition will be zero-valued over the second half of its range. Also, since the sampling period is now $T/2$, spectral magnitudes will increase by a factor of two consistent with Equation (4.1). Comparing the spectra of Figures 6.7(b) and 6.7(c), it is evident that Figure 6.7(c) can be obtained directly from 6.7(b) by eliminating every second $1/T$ Hz repetition and multiplying remaining components by a factor of two. This is essentially an ideal lowpass digital filtering operation that can be approximated either by direct digital filtering or by DFT/IDFT methods. In the case of direct filtering, $\{x[n]\}$ is first modified by adding a single zerovalued sample midway between each pair of existing T second samples. This operation does not modify the DTFT of $\{x[n]\}$ and therefore the spectrum of Figure 6.7(b) is unchanged but the sampling rate is effectively doubled moving the 'foldover' frequency from $1/2T$ Hz to $1/T$ Hz. A lowpass digital filter with a gain of two operating at a sampling rate of $2/T$ Hz can then be used to severely attenuate spectral components in the range $1/2T$ to $3/2T$ Hz obtaining a good approximation to the spectrum of Figure 6.7(c).

Interpolation can also be performed using DFT/IDFT methods to perform the lowpass filtering. The DFT of the original time sequence specifies N samples of the spectrum of Figure 6.7(b) in the range 0 to $1/T$ Hz whereas the DFT of the interpolated sequence specifies $2N$ samples of the spectrum of Figure 6.7(c) in the range 0 to $2/T$ Hz. The DFT of the interpolated sequence can therefore be constructed by doubling the number of samples of the original DFT and moving samples from the range $1/2T$ to $1/T$ Hz to the range $3/2T$ to $2/T$ Hz leaving zerovalued samples in the range $1/T$ to $3/2T$. The interpolated sequence itself is then obtained by doubling the values of the resulting set of $2N$ frequency samples and taking the IDFT.

The argument can be generalized for interpolation with values of I other than 0.5 by varying the number of extra zerovalued samples added to time or frequency sequences. For example, in the case of the direct filtering method, if $I = 1/S$ and S is an integer then a digital lowpass filter with gain S operating at a sampling rate of S/T Hz, cutoff $1/2T$ Hz and with $(S-1)$ zerovalued samples inserted between each pair of original samples, will generate an additional $(S-1)$ interpolated samples per input sample.

If a standard FFT algorithm is used for interpolation with N a power of 2, I is restricted to $1/2^K$ where K is an integer. This applies to Program 6.5 which performs time domain interpolation of real sequences with $I = 0.5, 0.25$, etc.

Program 6.5 INTERPOL: interpolation using FFT

```
10 REM INTERPOL
20 DEF FNA(X)=INT(10000*X+0.5)/10000
30 PRINT "TYPE X WHERE"
40 PRINT "INTERPOLATION FACTOR I=1/(2^X)";
50 INPUT X : PRINT "I=";1/(2^X)
60 PRINT "TYPE X WHERE NO. OF SAMPLES = 2^X"
70 INPUT M
80 NS=2^M : XO=2^X : NO=NS*XO
```

```
90 DIM XR(NO),XI(NO),SI(NO),CO(NO),X(NO)
100 PRINT "DEFINE INPUT SEQUENCE"
110 GOSUB 10000 : REM ARRAY DEFN. SUB.
120 FOR N=0 TO NS-1 : XR(N)=X(N) : XI(N)=0
130 NEXT N
140 IN=1 : GOSUB 30000 : REM FFT SUB.
150 M=M+X : NT=2^M : ND=NT-NS
160 FOR N=NS/2+1 TO NS-1
170 XR(N+ND)=XR(N) : XR(N)=0
180 XI(N+ND)=XI(N) : XI(N)=0
190 NEXT N
200 XR(NS/2)=XR(NS/2)/2 : XR(NS/2+ND)=XR(NS/2)
210 FOR N=0 TO NT-1
220 XR(N)=XR(N)*XO : XI(N)=XI(N)*XO
230 NEXT N
240 NS=NT : IN=-1 : GOSUB 30000 : REM FFT SUB.
250 PRINT "INTERPOLATED SEQUENCE"
260 FOR N=0 TO NT-1
270 PRINT FNA(XR(N));
280 NEXT N
290 END
10000 REM - - ARRAY DEFINITION SUB. - -
[- - etc. see Program 1.4 - -]

30000 REM - - FFT SUB. - -
[- - etc. see Program 6.1 - -]

Sample run

TYPE X WHERE
INTERPOLATION FACTOR I=1/(2^X)? 2
I = .25
TYPE X WHERE NO. OF SAMPLES = 2^X? 3
DEFINE INPUT SEQUENCE
SEQUENCE TYPE? UP
STARTING/ENDING SAMPLE NOS. ? 2,5
INTERPOLATED SEQUENCE
 0 -.096 -.1533 -.1283  0   .2222
 .5  .7778  1  1.1283  1.1533  1.096
 1  .9157  .8827  .9157  1  1.096
 1.1533  1.1283  1  .7778  .5  .2222
 0 -.1283 -.1533 -,096  0  .0843
 .1173  .0843
```

Program notes

(1) The program generates an NS-sample input sequence using subroutine 10000. The input is transformed using FFT subroutine 30000 and the resulting frequency samples appropriately scaled and shifted to form the $2^X \times$ NS sample DFT of the interpolated sequence. Application of the IDFT then generates the interpolated sequence.

(2) The sample run illustrates interpolation of the 'pulse', $\{0,0,1,1,1,1,0,0\}$ for $I = 0.25$ in which case an additional three

interpolating sample values appear between each pair of given values.

6.12.2 *Decimation*

In decimation, a sampling rate reduction is achieved by selecting every Ith sample of a sequence and discarding the others. If, for example, $I = 2$ and the spectrum of a given sequence $\{y[n]\}$ is as illustrated in Figure 6.7(c) then the decimated sequence formed by selecting every second sample of, $\{y[n]\}$, will be, $\{x[n]\}$, corresponding to the spectrum of Figure 6.7(b). The same argument can be applied to any sequence $\{y[n]\}$ for $I = 2$ and a sampling period of $T/2$ provided its spectrum is zero in the range from $1/2T$ to $1/T$ Hz. For $I = 2$, the sequence $\{y[n]\}$ can be uniquely represented by $\{x[n]\}$ only if $\{y[n]\}$ can be regarded as the samples of an analogue signal which has been bandlimited to a quarter of the sampling frequency in the first instance. This is quite consistent with the sampling theorem (see Section 4.2); if a signal is bandlimited to less than $1/2T$ Hz then $1/T$ Hz is the smallest sampling rate which can be used without aliasing error. If the higher sampling rate of $2/T$ Hz is used then twice the number of samples are generated half of which are strictly redundant.

To generalize, if decimation by a factor of I is required for a sequence with a sampling rate of $1/T$ samples/second then its spectrum must be zero in the range from $1/(2TI)$ Hz to $1/(2T)$ Hz to permit decimation at $1/(TI)$ samples per second with no aliasing error. This bandlimiting operation may be achieved by digital lowpass filtering using an FIR or IIR design or by FFT methods as discussed in Section 6.11.2. Finally, it should be noted that decimation can be combined with interpolation to obtain a wider range of values of I. For example, interpolation with $I = 0.5$ followed by decimation with $I = 3$ will be equivalent to decimation with $I = 1.5$.

6.13 Spectral analysis

The need for spectral analysis arises in a wide range of practical situations such as sound and vibration studies, radar and sonar systems and speech and image processing. Traditional analogue methods of spectral analysis can be very effectively replaced by digital signal processing using FFT methods. If an analogue signal is to be analysed then, to satisfy the sampling theorem, the sampling rate must be greater than twice the highest input frequency otherwise aliasing error will distort the spectrum as discussed in Section 4.4.1. Also, if the analogue input is prefiltered by an analogue lowpass filter in order to reduce aliasing to tolerable levels then some compensation of the DFT output values may be necessary since any practical lowpass filtering will cause some spectral distortion. A further difficulty is the 'picket-fence' effect arising because the DFT generates frequency samples only at discrete intervals. Evidence of spectral features, such as sharp peaks occuring between the frequency samples, may be lost or at least partly obscured. If this is a problem, interpolated frequency samples can be produced by adding extra zerovalued samples to the time sequence in much the same way as discussed for time domain interpolation in Section 6.12.1.

6.13.1 Windowing

Of particular importance is the effect of applying the DFT to a finite section or 'window' of a much longer sequence for which spectral analysis is required. For example, consider the problem of estimating the spectrum of an infinite sequence $\{x[n]\}$, by taking the DFT of N samples of the finite sequence, $\{x[n]\}_{0,N-1}$.

Setting $k = 0$ in Equation (6.1) gives an estimate, $X[0]$ of the spectral component at zero frequency, sometimes referred to as the 'dc component'; that is:

$$X[0] = \sum_{n=0}^{N-1} x[n] \tag{6.37}$$

This is identical to the output which would have been obtained by an FIR filter with input, $\{x[n]\}$ and impulse response, $\{h[n]\}$ consisting of N unit-valued samples:

$$h[n] = \begin{cases} 1, n = 0, 1, \ldots, (N-1) \\ 0, \text{ otherwise} \end{cases} \tag{6.38}$$

The output, $\{y[n]\}$, of this filter is given by the linear convolution:

$$y[n] = \sum_{r=0}^{N-1} h[r] x[n-r] \tag{6.39}$$

This is illustrated in Figure 6.8 for $N = 4$. Such a filter generates the nth 'sliding' estimate, $y[n]$ of the zero frequency component $X[0]$ on the basis of a block of N consecutive input samples from $x[n - N + 1]$ to $x[n]$. The particular output $y[n] = X[0]$ is obtained when $n = (N-1)$. Other outputs of this equivalent FIR filter correspond to the $X[0]$ value which the DFT would generate for other blocks of N consecutive input samples.

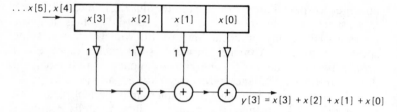

Figure 6.8 FIR filter equivalent of DFT output $x[0]$ for $N = 4$

The frequency response of the FIR filter associated with $X[0]$ is given by taking the DTFT of the impulse response, $\{h[n]\}$, as in Equation (6.38). That is:

$$H(e^{j\omega}) = \sum_{n=0}^{N-1} e^{-jn\omega} \tag{6.40}$$

This can be summed as a geometric series in $e^{-j\omega}$ in which case:

$$H(e^{j\omega}) = \frac{1 - e^{-jN\omega}}{1 - e^{-j\omega}}$$

$$= e^{-j(N-1)\omega/2} \left[\frac{\sin(N\omega/2)}{\sin(\omega/2)} \right] \tag{6.41}$$

The magnitude response, $|H(e^{j\omega})|$ is illustrated in Figure 6.9 for $N = 16$. Evidently this filter will be most responsive to a band of frequencies from $\omega = 0$ to almost $\omega = \pi/8$. It will certainly not respond only to a constant input of zero frequency. For example, a single input component of frequency $\pi/16$ will fall within the main response of $H(e^{j\omega})$ producing a nonzero value of $X[0]$ in the absence of any constant input. (This can be verified by using Program 6.1 to examine the DFT of various low-frequency sinusoidal sequences.) Such behaviour illustrates a fundamental limitation to spectral resolution obtainable using a finite window. In general, the $X[0]$ filter will be most responsive to frequencies up to about $\omega = 2\pi/N$. If N is made large this range can be made arbitrarily small but for N finite it will never be possible to properly resolve frequencies within this band.

DFT outputs other than $X[0]$ can be interpreted as FIR filter outputs in much the same way. The kth output is given by:

$$X[k] = \sum_{n=0}^{N-1} x[n] e^{-j2\pi nk/N} \tag{6.42}$$

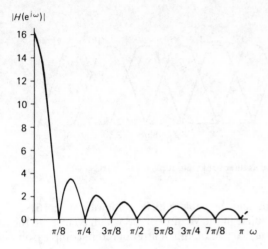

$|H(e^{j\omega})|$

Figure 6.9 Equivalent DFT magnitude response for output $X[0]$ for N = 16

and by generalizing the argument above, $X[k]$ can be interpreted as the output of filter for any given value of k with the complex impulse response:

$$h[n] = e^{-j2\pi k(N-1-n)/N} \quad n = 0, 1, \ldots, (N-1) \qquad (6.43)$$

The corresponding magnitude response can then be shown to be (Reference 4):

$$|H(e^{j\omega})| = \left| \frac{\sin[N(\omega - \omega')/2]}{\sin[(\omega - \omega')/2]} \right| \qquad (6.44)$$

where $\omega' = 2\pi k/N$. This response has the same shape as in Figure 6.9 but is now translated to ω'. The complete set of DFT outputs can therefore be regarded as the outputs of a filter bank with frequency responses which are represented in Figure 6.10 for $N = 16$. (Sidelobe responses are omitted in Figure 6.10 for clarity.) It is evident that frequency components closer together than about $\pi/8$, or $2\pi/N$ in general, will not be properly resolved in a DFT output sequence. Also, all filters can respond to a wide range of frequencies other than their centre frequencies due to their sidelobe responses. This 'spilling over' of responses from one frequency cell to another is termed 'leakage' and, with high levels of sidelobe ripple, can lead to quite misleading spectral estimates. For example, the filter associated with $X[0]$ in Figure 6.10 will respond to a strong

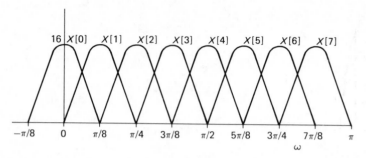

Figure 6.10 DFT regarded as filter bank output ($N = 16$)

frequency component near the peak of its first sidelobe at $3\pi/16$ (see Figure 6.9) but a response in the vicinity of $\pi/8$ which is closer to the nominal response at $\omega = 0$ will be much attenuated in comparison.

6.13.2 Window functions

A DFT input sequence can be regarded as a 'true' input, $\{x[n]\}$ multiplied by the N-sample rectangular window sequence $\{r[n]\}$ as discussed in Section 5.5. If $\{z[n]\}_{0,N-1}$ is the DFT input sequence then:

$$z[n] = r[n]x[n] \quad n = 0, 1, \ldots, (N-1) \tag{6.45}$$

The impulse response of the filter associated with $X[k]$ can now be expressed as, $r[n]h[n]$, $n = 0, 1, \ldots, (N-1)$ where $h[n]$ is defined by Equation (6.43). Because $r[n] = 1$ for $n = 0, 1, \ldots, (N-1)$, the impulse response is given by Equation (6.43) as before and therefore the shape of the frequency responses of the filter bank is unaltered. However, if other window functions are used as discussed in Section 5.5 it becomes possible to reduce the sidelobe ripple of a response such as Figure 6.9 at the expense of cutoff rate. Thus leakage can be reduced at the expense of frequency resolution since sidelobe reduction will be accompanied by an increase in the effective bandwidth of each filter.

6.14 References

1. Cooley, J. W. and Tukey, J. W. (April 1965) An algorithm for the machine computation of complex Fourier series. *Math Comp.* *19*, 297–301
2. Carlson, A. B. (1975) *Communication Systems*, McGraw-Hill
3. *Programs for Digital Signal Processing*, (1979) IEEE Press

4. Rabiner, L. R. and Gold, B. (1975) *Theory and Application of Digital Signal Processing*, Prentice-Hall
5. Ziener, R. E., Tranter, I. W. and Fannin, D. R. (1983) *Signals and Systems*, Macmillan

Problems

(6.1) Evaluate the DFT of the following 4-sample sequences using direct evaluation [Equation (6.1)]. Check using Program 6.1.

$$\{1,1,0,0\} \quad \{\cos(n\pi/2)\}_{0,3} \quad \{\sin(n\pi/2)\}_{0,3}$$

(6.2) Show that the DFT of the cosine sequence $\{\cos(2\pi nk/N)\}_{0,N-1}$ is always real and the DFT of the sine sequence $\{\sin(2\pi nk/N)\}_{0,N-1}$ is always purely imaginary. What property applies to a sequence which can be expressed as a sum of (a) cosine sequences (b) sine sequences. What conclusions can be drawn about their respective DFTs?

(6.3) Check the operation of Program 6.1 by taking the IDFT of the DFT of various input sequences (Program 6.1 can be easily modified to avoid typing in IDFT values).

(6.4) Prove by an argument similar to that of Section 6.4.1, that multiplying samples of a finite time sequence, $\{x[n]\}$ by $e^{j2\pi nL/N}$ is equivalent to a circular shift of $\{X[k]\}$ by L places (This relationship is known as the modulation theorem, see Reference 2). Demonstrate in terms of both time and frequency domain sequences that no operation occurs if $L = N$. Predict the effect on the spectrum of a sequence of changing the sign of every second sample and verify using Program 6.1.

(6.5) Show that the energy of a sequence of N samples:

$$\sum_{n=0}^{N-1} |x[n]|^2$$

can also be expressed in terms of its DFT as:

$$\frac{1}{N}\sum_{k=0}^{N-1} |X[k]|^2$$

(Hint: first express $|x[n]|^2$ as $x[n]x^*[n]$ in the LHS. Modify Program 6.1 to verify this relationship. This is one form of a relationship known as Parseval's theorem).

(6.6) Repeat problem (6.1) but evaluate using the FFT decimation in time FFT algorithm.

(6.7) Use Program 6.1 to verify the following DFT properties choosing test sequences and sample numbers so that the results are easily predicted. (i) Spectral symmetry for real signals (see Section 6.2.1). (ii) DFT of a circular shift, (6.10). (iii) Circular convolution, (6.13).

(**6.8**) Time Program 6.1 for a range of sequence lengths including the largest your computer can handle. Compare execution times using direct evaluation (see Program 2.2). Consider carefully how calculation of the twiddle factors will affect the comparison.

(**6.9**) Modify Program 6.1 to generate Fourier series coefficients as suggested in Section 6.9.1.

(**6.10**) The decimation in time algorithm (see Section 6.6.1) forms the DFT of a $2N$ sample sequence from the DFTs of two $N/2$ sample sequences formed by even and odd indices. Modify Program 6.3 so that the DFT of a single real $2N$-sample sequence may be computed by a single N sample DFT.

(**6.11**) Use Program 6.2 to investigate the approximation of a square wave by more harmonics than used in the sample run. In what sense does the approximation improve as the number of harmonics increases? (see Reference 5 for discussion of 'Gibbs phenomonen').

(**6.12**) Use Program 6.4 to implement the following difference equations. Choose input sequences so that outputs are easily predicted and checked.

(a) $y[n] = x[n] + x[n-1]$
(b) $y[n] = x[n] + 3x[n-1] + 3x[n-2] + x[n-3]$
(c) $y[n] = x[n-3]$

(**6.13**) Modify Program 6.4 to implement fast FIR filtering using the overlap save method.

(**6.14**) Modify Program 6.1 so that a Kaiser window (see Section 5.5) is applied to the input sequence before taking the DFT. Determine the magnitude response for $k = N/4$ by evaluating $|X[N/4]|$ for the complex input, $\{e^{j\omega n}\}$ and various values of ω.

Appendix

Analogue system theory

A linear time invariant (LTI) analogue system as represented in Figure A.1 is characterized by the following convolution formula:

$$y(t) = \int_{-\infty}^{\infty} h(\tau) x(t - \tau) \, d\tau \qquad (A.1)$$

where $x(t)$ is any input signal, $y(t)$ is the output signal and $h(t)$ is the impulse response, i.e. the theoretical response to $\delta(t)$ as defined in Chapter 2. This formula may be derived in the same way as discrete time convolution in Section 3.6 (see References 1,2,3) and the similarity between the two types of convolution may be observed. The same notation is used:

$$y(t) = h(t) * x(t) \qquad (A.2)$$

or equivalently:

$$y(t) = x(t) * h(t) = \int_{-\infty}^{\infty} x(\tau) h(t - \tau) \, d\tau \qquad (A.3)$$

A stable and causal analogue LTI system must satisfy:

$$\int_{-\infty}^{\infty} |h(t)| \, dt = \text{finite} \qquad \text{(stability)} \qquad (A.4)$$

$$h(t) = 0 \text{ for } t < 0 \qquad \text{(causality)} \qquad (A.5)$$

these conditions again being similar to those for digital systems. By Equation (A.1), the response to the complex exponential signal:

$$x(t) = e^{st} \qquad (A.6)$$

Figure A.1

where s is any complex number with real part greater than or equal to zero is:

$$y(t) = \int_{-\infty}^{\infty} h(\tau) \, e^{s(t-\tau)} \, d\tau = e^{st} H(s) \qquad (A.7)$$

where:

$$H(s) = \int_{-\infty}^{\infty} h(\tau) \, e^{-s\tau} \, d\tau \qquad (A.8)$$

For a causal system:

$$H(s) = \int_{0}^{\infty} h(t) \, e^{-st} \, dt \quad \text{(Laplace transform)} \qquad (A.9)$$

and is referred to as the Laplace transform of $h(t)$. Let $s = \sigma + j\Omega$. By the stability condition (A.4) it may be shown that for a causal and stable system, $H(s)$ must be finite for any value of s with $\sigma \geq 0$.

Classical design theory for LTI analogue circuits operating below about 100 MHz is generally based on concepts of lumped parameter resistance, capacitance and inductance as described by standard differential equations relating current and voltage. Analysis of such circuits gives a relationship between input signal $x(t)$ and output signal $y(t)$ in the form of a linear differential equation expressable in the following form:

$$b_0 y(t) + b_1 \frac{dy(t)}{dt} + b_2 \frac{d^2 y(t)}{dt^2} + \ldots + b_M \frac{d^M y(t)}{dt^M}$$

$$= a_0 x(t) + a_1 \frac{dx(t)}{dt} + a_2 \frac{d^2 x(t)}{dt^2} + \ldots + b_N \frac{d^N x(t)}{dt^N} \qquad (A.10)$$

The order of this differential equation is M or N depending on which number is greater. When $x(t) = e^{st}$ with σ (real part of s) ≥ 0, $y(t) = H(s) \, e^{st}$ and:

$$\frac{dx(t)}{dt} = s \, e^{st}, \qquad \frac{d^2 x(t)}{dt^2} = s^2 \, e^{st}, \qquad \frac{dy(t)}{dt} = sH(s) \, e^{st} \quad \text{etc.}$$

where $H(s)$ is defined by Equation (A.8) in terms of the impulse response, $h(t)$, of the circuit. It follows by substituting in Equation (A.10) that:

$$H(s) \, e^{st} (a_0 + b_1 s + b_2 s^2 + \ldots + b_M s^M)$$

$$= e^{st} (a_0 + a_1 s + \ldots + a_N s^N)$$

Therefore:

$$H(s) = \frac{a_0 + a_1 s + a_2 s^2 + \ldots + a_N s^N}{b_0 + b_1 s + b_2 s^2 + \ldots + b_M s^M} \qquad (A.11)$$

provided the denominator is non-zero. A zero denominator would make $H(s)$ infinite (discounting the possibility of the numerator being exactly zero also). Equation (A.11) is equivalent to Equation (A.9) for a causal stable LTI analogue circuit when $\sigma \geq 0$ since $H(s)$ must be finite. The expression obtained is referred to as the system or transfer function. When $\sigma = 0$, e^{st} becomes $e^{j\Omega t} = \cos \Omega t + j \sin \Omega t$ and the response to such an input signal would be:

$$y(t) = H(j\Omega) e^{j\Omega t} \qquad (A.12)$$

where:

$$H(j\Omega) = \int_{-\infty}^{\infty} h(t) e^{-j\Omega t} dt \quad \text{(frequency response)} \qquad (A.13)$$

$H(j\Omega)$ is the 'frequency response' of the analogue system and is identical to the Fourier transform of the impulse response $h(t)$ (see Equation (2.14)). The stability condition (A.4) ensures that $H(j\Omega)$ is finite. The modulus and phase of $H(j\Omega)$ determine the response to a sinusoidal input of frequency Ω and it may be shown that the response to an input signal $x(t) = A \cos (\Omega t + \phi)$, will be:

$$y(t) = A\, G(\Omega) \cos (\Omega t + \phi + \theta(\Omega)) \qquad (A.14)$$

where:

$$G(\Omega) = |H(j\Omega)| \text{ and } \theta(\Omega) = \arg (H(j\Omega)) \qquad (A.15)$$

$G(\Omega)$ is the 'gain' and $\theta(\Omega)$ is the 'phase' of the analogue system.
The group delay of an analogue system is defined as

$$T_G(\Omega) = \frac{-d\theta(\Omega)}{d\Omega} \qquad (A.16)$$

and is the slope of the phase lag response at any frequency Ω. For a linear phase system:

$$\theta(\Omega) = -k\Omega \qquad (A.17)$$

for some constant k and therefore $T_G(\Omega) = k$ for all values of Ω.

Factorizing the numerator and denominator polynominals of $H(s)$ as given by Equation (A.11),

$$H(s) = K \frac{(s - z_1)(s - z_2) \dots (s - z_N)}{(s - p_1)(s - p_2) \dots (s - p_M)} \qquad (A.18)$$

where $z_1, z_2, \dots, z_N$ are referred to as the zeros of $H(s)$ and $p_1, p_2, \dots, p_M$ are the poles of $H(s)$. For a causal stable system, the fact that $H(s)$ must be finite for $\sigma \geq 0$ means that all poles must have negative real parts.

Plotting pole and zeros of $H(s)$ on an Argand diagram with horizontal axis σ and vertical axis Ω, it follows that all poles must lie to the left of the imaginary $(j\Omega)$ axis if $H(s)$ is to represent a causal and stable system. No restrictions need be placed on the zeros.

It is often convenient to combine poles and zeros into pairs and thus express $H(s)$ as the product of 'biquadratic' transfer functions each of the form

$$H_i(s) = \frac{A_{0i} + A_{1i}s + A_{2i}s^2}{B_{0i} + B_{1i}s + B_{2i}s^2} \qquad (A.19)$$

The gain and phase response of a filter whose transfer function is expressed in this way may be analysed by means of Program A.1 below. $H(s)$ is said to be a serial cascade of biquadratic transfer functions. This expression for $H(s)$ may be converted into parallel form consisting of the sum of biquadratic transfer functions and a constant K. Program A.2 performs this conversion provided the poles of $H(s)$ are distinct.

Program A.1 HSAN: frequency response of $H(s)$ expressed as serial cascade

```
10   REM HSAN FREQ RESP OF H(S)
20   DIM A0(8),A1(8),A2(8),B0(8),B1(8),B2(8)
25   DEF FNR(X)=INT(X*1000+0.5)/1000
30   PRINT"NUMBER OF SECTNS:"; : INPUT NS
40   FOR J=1 TO NS
50   PRINT"ENTER COEFFS FOR SECTN ";J
60   PRINT"A0,A1,A2: "; : INPUT A0(J),A1(J),A2(J)
70   PRINT"B0,B1,B2: "; : INPUT B0(J),B1(J),B2(J)
80   NEXT J : PRINT"OK"
90   PRINT"ENTER W0,W1,WI: "; : INPUT W0,W1,WI
100  PRINT : W=W0
110  PRINT"W RAD/SEC"," GAIN DB"," PHASE LAG DEG"
120  R1=1 : I1=0 : R2=1 : I2=0
130  FOR J=1 TO NS
140  R=A0(J)-A2(J)*W*W : I=A1(J)*W
150  S=R1*R-I1*I : I1=R1*I+I1*R : R1=S
160  R=B0(J)-B2(J)*W*W : I=B1(J)*W
```

```
170 S=R2*R-I2*I : I2=R2*I+I2*R : R2=S
180 NEXT J
190 GOSUB 600 : REM GET G & P
200 PRINT FNR(W),FNR(G),FNR(-P*57.29578)
210 W=W+WI
220 IF W<W1+WI THEN GOTO 120
230 STOP
600 REM SUBROUTINE TO CALC GAIN,PHAS OF
610 REM (R1+J*I1)/(R2+J*I2) IN DB,RADS
620 REM AS FOR PROGRAM 3.4
```

Sample run

```
NUMBER OF SECTNS:? 2
ENTER COEFFS FOR SECTN 1
A0,A1,A2:?1, 0,0
B0,B1,B2:?1, 0.76537, 1
ENTER COEFFS FOR SECTN 2
A0,A1,A2:?1, 0,0
B0,B1,B2:?1, 1.84776, 1
OK
ENTER W0,W1,WI:?0,4,0.2
```

W RAD/SEC	GAIN DB	PHASE LAG DEG
0	0	0
0.2	0	30.114
0.4	-0.003	61.369
0.6	-0.072	95.664
0.8	-0.674	135.859
1.0	-3.01	180
1.2	-7.243	216.822
.	.	.
.	.	.
.	.	.
4.0	-48.023	323.171

Program notes

(1) Once the coefficients for each section have been entered, the user must supply a starting frequency (WO), a final frequency (W1) and an increment (WI), all in radians per second. These parameters determine the range of the frequency response table and the number of entries.

(2) The sample run analyses the fourth order Butterworth low pass system function (cut-off frequency 1 radian/sec) designed by running Program 3.3 in Section 5.10.5.

Program A.2 *SERPAR: serial to parallel conversion*

```
10  REM SERPAR:  SERIAL TO PARALLEL
20  DIM A0(8),A1(8),A2(8),B0(8),B1(8),B2(8)
30  PRINT"NUMBER OF SECTIONS:"; : INPUT NS
40  FOR J=1 TO NS
```

```
 50  PRINT"ENTER COEFFS FOR SERIAL SECTN ";J
 60  PRINT"A0,A1,A2:"; : INPUT A0(J),A1(J),A2(J)
 70  PRINT"B0,B1,B2:"; : INPUT B0(J),B1(J),B2(J)
 80  NEXT J :PRINT : K=1
 90  FOR J=1 TO NS
100  IF B2(J)=0 THEN GOTO 210
110  K=K*A2(J)/B2(J) : P=-B1(J)/B2(J)/2
120  Q=(B1(J)/B2(J)/2)^2-B0(J)/B2(J)
130  IF Q>0 THEN GOTO 170
140  IF ABS(Q)<1E-10 THEN GOTO 430
150  R=P : I=SQR(-Q) : GOSUB 290
160  P0=R1-R*I1/I : P1=I1/I : GOTO 260
170  Q=SQR(Q) : R=P+Q:I=0 : GOSUB 290 : RT=R1
180  R=P-Q : GOSUB 290 : P1=(RT-R1)/Q/2
190  P0=(R1*(P+Q)-RT*R)/Q/2
200  GOTO 260
210  IF B1(J)=0 THEN GOTO 250
220  K=K*A1(J)/B1(J) : R=-B0(J)/B1(J)
230  I=0 : GOSUB 290 : P0=R1 : P1=0
240  GOTO 260
250  K=K*A0(J)/B0(J) : P0=0 : P1=0
260  PRINT"PARALLEL SECTION ";J;":-"
261  PRINT"A0: ";P0," B0: ";B0(J)
262  PRINT"A1: ";P1," B1: ";B1(J)
263  PRINT"A2: ";0," B2: ";B2(J)
270  NEXT J : PRINT : PRINT"K=";K
280  STOP
290  REM SUBROUTINE EVAL
300  R1=1 : I1=0
310  FOR L=1 TO NS
320  R2=A0(L)+A1(L)*R+A2(L)*(R*R-I*I)
330  I2=A1(L)*I+2*A2(L)*R*I
340  M=R1*R2-I1*I2 : I1=I1*R2+R1*I2 : R1=M
350  R2=B0(L)+B1(L)*R+B2(L)*(R*R-I*I)
360  I2=B1(L)*I+2*B2(L)*R*I
370  IF L=J THEN GOTO 420
380  M=R2*R2+I2*I2
390  IF M<1E-12 THEN GOTO 430
400  R2=R2/M : I2=-I2/M
410  M=R1*R2-I1*I2 : I1=I1*R2+R1*I2 : R1=M
420  NEXT L : RETURN
430  PRINT"FAILS:  REPEATED POLES" : STOP
```

Sample run

```
NUMBER OF SECTIONS:? 2
ENTER COEFFS FOR SERIAL SECTN 1
A0,A1,A2:? 1, 0, 0
B0,B1,B2:? 1, 0.76537, 1
ENTER COEFFS FOR SERIAL SECTN 2
A0,A1,A2:?1,0,0
B0,B1,B2:?1,1.84776,1

PARALLEL SECTION 1:-
A0: -0.70711 B0: 1
A1: -0.92388 B1: 0.76537
A2: 0         B2: 1
```

```
PARALLEL SECTION 2:-
A0: 1.70711   B0: 1
A1: 0.92388   B1: 1.84776
A2: 0         B2: 1
K= 0
```

Program notes

(1) The user must specify the coefficients for each section of $H(s)$ expressed as a serial cascade, i.e. $H(s) = H_1(s) H_2(s) \dots H_N(s)$. The program re-expresses $H(s)$ in the form:

$$H(s) = K + H_1(s) + H_2(s) + \dots + H_N(s)$$

by a partial fraction method which requires all the poles of $H(s)$ to be distinct.

(2) The sample run converts the serial expression for $H(s)$ analysed by Program A1 (fourth-order Butterworth lowpass) into parallel form.

(3) This program may also be used to convert a digital system function $H(z)$, expressed as a serial cascade, into parallel form.

References

1. Faulkner, E. A. (1969) *Introduction to the Theory of Linear Systems*, Chapman and Hall
2. Papoulis, A. (1980) *Circuits and Systems: A Modern Approach*, Holt-Saunders
3. Meade M. L. and Dillon C. R. (1986) *Signals and Systems*, Van Nostrand Reinhold

Index